Cosmology Crisis Cleared
David Michalets

Self-published **on November 27, 2021**

Table of Contents

Introduction

Cosmology Crisis Cleared identifies the fundamental mistake causing the failure of cosmologists to agree on a value for Hubble's Constant, which is the most important constant in cosmology. After 80 years of trying, this is a crisis.
The crisis revolves around the uncertainty of Hubble's Constant. The University of Chicago in "The Hubble constant, explained" has a clear statement of this constant's importance in this crisis:

The Hubble constant is one of the most important numbers in cosmology because it tells us how fast the universe is expanding, which can be used to determine the age of the universe and its history. It gets its name from UChicago alum Edwin Hubble, who was first to calculate the constant from his measurements of stars in 1929.
Despite nearly a hundred years of astronomical measurements and calculations, scientists still can't agree on the exact value of the Hubble constant. The true number could reveal missing pieces in our understanding of physics, like new particles or a new form of dark energy. [R4]

Excerpt from a 2021 news story, titled "Why is there a 'crisis' in cosmology?"

Since 2014, there have been over 300 proposals for solutions to this "crisis in cosmology." None of these proposals is universally agreed upon by cosmologists, and as measurements continue, the crisis just keeps getting worse. [R4]

This book explains those incorrect measurements. The essential problem for astronomers is finding an acceptable velocity for an acceptable distance to calculate an acceptable value of Hubble's Constant.

This book describes the pivotal, initial mistake made by an astronomer, Vesto Slipher, in 1912 which is the basis for the eventual crisis.
By cosmology accepting and never fixing the initial mistake, more mistakes followed, because the initial mistake persisted rather than being removed from practice to prevent any subsequent use. Cosmology has remained in a crisis mode because new measurements continue to come from a wrong procedure. Calculating Hubble's Constant requires consistent velocities. Eventually, cosmologists declared a crisis when alternate distance metrics and alternate redshift metrics could not achieve the same value. No one questioned the actual measurement procedure of a redshift velocity.

After reviewing the data compiled for this book, I conclude that every galaxy and quasar has its motion measured incorrectly. The mistake in this measurement is driven by one wrong assumption: that the velocity of a galaxy or quasar can measured from a spectrum by the same technique as used for a star in the Milky Way.

The method of measuring a velocity by only a simple change in a spectrum CANNOT apply to a star as well as a galaxy or quasar.
Only a star of the 3 has a photosphere surface for attached atoms.
I can explain why the method being used since the first measurement of a galaxy velocity is wrong. Unfortunately, its use persists to this day. The first measurement of a

galaxy velocity was by the astronomer Vesto Slipher in 1912; it was a redshift.

The first galaxy blue shift velocity was measured by Slipher in 1914.

Cosmologists have accepted both the measurements and their method, but because the values are wrong by the wrong technique, these velocities can force awkward explanations.

Astronomers are apparently unwilling to question the validity of their measurements though sometimes the values are near impossible. For example, in recent decades velocities much greater than the speed of light are measured and accepted.

The redshift is a proportional change in a wavelength. This ratio is assigned to the value of z ratio. The value of z can be converted into a velocity by multiplying z times c, or the velocity of light. the value of z = 1 means the velocity of the object driving the change in the spectrum by the Doppler effect was moving at the speed of light.

There are many galaxies and quasars with measured velocities of z> 1. The galaxy having the highest measured redshift is GN-Z11 with z=11.

In my opinion, one's first response to any value of z>1 should be:

"This superluminal velocity is impossible for a massive galaxy, so its measurement must be a mistake."

That the superluminal velocity is impossible should not be debated.

Many galaxies have billions of stars.
Our Milky Way has over 200 billion stars, and M31 has 1 trillion stars.
A force was required to accelerate the individual stars into motion; then, the force must be maintained to reach a particular velocity, based on the force and mass. Power is a total of the force applied over a time duration.

The power required for a single galaxy to attain a superluminal velocity needs no calculation when the result is worthless in a rational discussion.

Unfortunately, cosmologists accepted these ridiculous velocity values and proposed explanations for them.
These border on ridiculous also.
They proposed: a) a fabric of space expanding at a velocity greater than the velocity of light,
b) dark energy (the word dark is for either unmeasurable or imaginary) for the individual galaxy trajectories, and
c) a big bang explosion, which is just a creation story.

If the mistake is not fixed, then part of the foundation of cosmology is invalid meaning all that rests on it will fail.

This book analyzes the public data of over 600 galaxies.

Each galaxy has measurements to obtain its position and magnitude. When possible, its light is measured as a spectrum. The spectrum represents the energy distribution of the light among its continuum of wavelengths. For many years, the change in a spectrum was measured using spectroscopy. The change in wavelength distribution was assumed to be caused by the Doppler Effect. In recent decades, sky surveys have captured images of many galaxies, so their individual magnitudes can be measured.

When the spectrum is used to measure a change. this change is sometimes called a redshift, which can be used to calculate a velocity and distance, based on certain assumptions.

This quantity of images resulted in using other methods of data analysis to obtain a distance based on luminosity where light dims by distance. These methods do not rely only on specific wavelengths in a spectrum to derive a galaxy's velocity and to then derive its distance. Each method has important assumptions for its calculation. All the non-Doppler methods which calculate a distance also assume a galaxy's velocity can be calculated from its distance based on Hubble's Law.

In 1923, Hubble confirmed the first galaxy being outside our Milky Way. Before that event, distant spiral nebulae could be either inside or beyond our Milky Way.

Measurements of galaxies have been continuing for about 100 years, with many including its spectrum. These measurements lead to estimated velocities and distances. Several assumptions affect the conclusions being drawn from the raw data. Those assumptions are crucial and must be reconsidered after a review of the historical data and the nuances of the Doppler Effect.

There are more galaxies in the universe, but the others would not affect the conclusions based on this diverse set of those close enough for a spectrum analysis.

Among the goals after analyzing the data of these galaxies:

a) Define the correct procedure for measuring a velocity of galaxy or quasar,

b) Describe the origin and future of Hubble-Lemaitre Law and its Hubble's Constant;
c) Evaluate the alternate methods used for getting a redshift not from the spectrum, like based on luminosity changes.
d) Evaluate the various methods for calculating an object's distance from changes in luminosity, like using Cepheids.

After revealing the cause of the crisis with Hubble's constant, its new role in cosmology is described.

With this crisis in cosmology resolved, a clearer picture of the universe is revealed, regarding valid motions and distances of galaxies and quasars.

The big bang theory arose from galaxy measurements beginning over 100 years ago. This theory must be revised after correct velocity measurements.

My research created an archive of data for each galaxy, to enable charts of certain values, and to support the conclusions.

This is a summary of the 18 sections:

1)   Defining the Crisis describes the crisis in general terms and references conferences for cosmologist to discuss a resolution.

2)   Data Sets describes my compilation of galaxy data. The 2 main references are Wikipedia and NASA Extragalactic Database, or NED. The data cover more than 600 galaxies, with their constellation, celestial coordinates, magnitude, red shift velocity, distance, and diameter (when available), in either light-years or minutes of arc. Over 20 Abell galaxy clusters are included for reference. Please note some screen captures of NED's transient display pages are provided to show its content when helpful. There is no permanent page for a link, for a later reference. Those images were reduced in size for this page size. To see the original NED data, one must use the NED web site.

3)   Light describes several forms of electromagnetic radiation, or light, including synchrotron and thermal.

4)   Doppler Effect describes one of the fundamental interpretations of a change measured in a spectrum. One must be sure of where in the light's path did the change occur. Sometimes, a mistake is made. A star must use a method unlike a galaxy or quasar.

5)   Star Vs Galaxy describes the differences between them, which require different methods to obtain their velocity

6)   Stars describes a star's light generation mechanism and a few relevant types of stars including variable stars having a consistent pattern between brighter and dimmer.

7)   Galaxies offers basic descriptions of galaxies and their types.

8)   Galaxies with Cepheids details the combination of velocity and distance for each galaxy having 1 or more Cepheids.

9)   Quasars describes another distant celestial object which is neither a star nor galaxy. Quasars are far fewer in number than galaxies. They must be included because they are part of the perceived expansion.

10)   Cosmic Distance Ladder describes the priority assigned to the respective distance calculation methods.

11)   NED Redshifts describes the different redshift behaviors being measured for galaxies to measure its velocity. Any velocity is often assumed to be related to its distance by Hubble's Law. That assumption must be questioned with new velocities.

12)   NED Distances describes the respective methods for calculating a distance.

13)   Hubble's Law or the Hubble-Lemaitre Law describes the formula relating a distant object's velocity to its distance.

14) Hubble's Constant is claimed to represent the rate of expansion; a few years ago, cosmologists declared a crisis when they could not agree on its value and with their desired precision.

15) Charts presents charts of the basic data, like magnitude, velocity, and distance, or which galaxies are using the different redshift methods. These charts illustrate the justification for some conclusions

16) Bang describes this theory which includes universe expansion. This theory is affected by the changes in Hubble's Constant and universe expansion. A cosmological model arose to explain the big bang process from an explosion through the evolution of the debris.

17) Final Conclusion summarizes the book's conclusions.

18) All external references in the book have links available as directed here.

For example, when a paragraph on page 13 has an on-line reference, then [R13] is shown after that paragraph. This enables the reader to check the entire original source using the references web page for this book, when the source is of interest. During the first read-through, the interruption to a reference is probably avoided.

1 Defining the crisis

This book's introduction included a statement from the University of Chicago about the uncertainty of Hubble's Constant.
It is repeated here, followed by an observation.

The Hubble constant is one of the most important numbers in cosmology because it tells us how fast the universe is expanding, which can be used to determine the age of the universe and its history. It gets its name from UChicago alum Edwin Hubble, who was first to calculate the constant from his measurements of stars in 1929.

Despite nearly a hundred years of astronomical measurements and calculations, scientists still can't agree on the exact value of the Hubble constant. The true number could reveal missing pieces in our understanding of physics, like new particles or a new form of dark energy. [R4]

Observation:

The University of Chicago is wrong with their claim Hubble was first to do the calculation.

Georges Lemaître published his formula in 1926 based on the galaxy data at the time.

In 2018, his contribution to Hubble's Law was recognized by the AUI changing its name to Hubble–Lemaître law.

From a 2019 story titled "A Crisis in Cosmology – Measurements of Hubble Constant Disagree"

"Therein lies the crisis in cosmology," says Fassnacht. "While the Hubble Constant is constant everywhere in space at a given time, it is not constant in time. So, when we are comparing the Hubble Constants that come out of various techniques, we are comparing the early universe (using distant observations) vs. the late, more modern part of the universe (using local, nearby observations)." [R15]

Excerpt from a 2021 news story "Why is there a 'crisis' in cosmology?"

Since 2014, there have been over 300 proposals for solutions to this "crisis in cosmology." None of these proposals is universally agreed upon by cosmologists, and as measurements continue, the crisis just keeps getting worse. [R15]

Observation:

The calculation of Hubble's constant requires 2 factors: 1) velocity, and 2) a distance.

The introduction already noted the velocity of a galaxy or quasar is measured wrong.
Therefore, these studies are using wrong values for the first factor.

This is explained in Section Star vs Galaxy.

2 Data Sets

I compiled data into a large data set to support this book's conclusions. To make sure this analysis was not skewed by a single source, two were used.

The book uses 2 references: Wikipedia or NASA/IPAC Extragalactic Database. Or NED. This reference site will be just NED in this book. Unfortunately, the 2 references do not agree in all galaxies.

Though there are many galaxies having an assigned NGC number, only those galaxies having defined celestial coordinates are listed. The galaxies are entered by increasing right ascension values in each constellation, which are in order by their sky quadrant.

Those galaxies having no velocity and distance values are sometimes omitted as they offer nothing to the analysis. Some were entered, though lacking those values, when their presence in the cluster's data contributes to the analysis of angular separation between consecutive galaxies within a cluster.

Galaxies are in order of quadrant, then increasing RA through each of the constellations in the quadrant.

2.1 Wikipedia Layout

Wikipedia has a general format for a galaxy's data. At the top of the page is general information. Sometimes, the data of interest, like distance, could be found here. Sometimes the value will match or disagree with its later value.

Some galaxies will have an image to the right of the description.
The right side of the page will have the galaxy's celestial coordinates, at the top, or below the image.

Each galaxy will have Redshift data, as one or more velocities.

Many will have one or both of a z value or a km/s value. The km/s value must match z multiplied by 3E5 or else one or both is a mistake.

There can be a helio radial velocity; this is the one to use. NED also uses this term.
There can be a galactocentric velocity; this value is not for this analysis, so ignore it.

Below the velocities, there is usually a Distance. It will be stated in Mly, or Mpc or both. Since Hubble's constant uses Mpc so does the Data Set.

Next, there should be the visual magnitude, as Apparent magnitude (V). This is the value of interest for a luminosity. There could be other values, such as Absolute (A) or bolometric (B), but none are used in this analysis of redshifts.

Next are the galaxy Characteristics.

These include the Type. This is used for every galaxy.

Some references will have its size, stated as either a linear dimension in lightyears or parsecs, or as one or more angular dimensions, usually in moa, or minutes of arc, or arcminutes. Sometimes, arcseconds are used.

Some galaxies offer more data, such as an estimated mass, or star count but none of these are used in a redshift analysis. Some are probably based on assumptions with a distance and size.

2.2 NED Layout of galaxy data

The NASA/IPAC Extragalactic Database (NED) is funded by the National Aeronautics and Space Administration and operated by the California Institute of Technology. [R20]

NED has a general format for a galaxy's data. At the top of the page is a series of tabs. Each title is followed by a number inside (), where the number indicates the number of items available after this selection.

The relevant tabs are:

- Redshifts
- Spectra
- Distances

Redshifts should include the number of lines indicated, but only 2 are used:
V (heliocentric) has the value in km/s.

D (Local Group) has the value in Mpc.

The Wikipedia velocity and distance values should match NED, unless I used either when the sites were not synchronized.

The Spectra selection shows the number of spectra indicated by ().

Unfortunately, NED never explicitly identifies which specific spectrum was used for the stated redshift value in that tab's line.

2.3 NED Example with NGC 3226

Showing an example might make the descriptions clearer, because it has data available for its tabs.

Here is a sequence of screen captures. Links to the original images are not available because NED is interactive with no permanent links for transient pages of data.

2.3.1 Image 1

NGC 3226 is entered in the box and the Go button is selected.

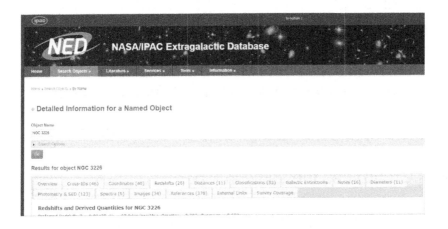

There is usually a delay between Go and the display of: Results for object, with the bar having the tab selections.

2.3.2 Image 2

Selecting the Redshifts tab shows its data. The legend indicates 26 lines for this galaxy.

Redshifts and Derived Quantities for NGC 3226

Preferred Redshift: Z = 0.00439, H₀ = 67.8 km/sec/Mpc, Ωmatter = 0.308, Qvacuum = 0.692

Quantities Derived from Preferred Redshift for NGC 3226

Calculated and Corrected Velocities

Type	Velocities	Reference View References in ADS
V (Heliocentric)	1315 ± 5 km/s	2011MNRAS.413..813C
V (Kinematic LSR)	1312 ± 5 km/s	1988MNRAS.221.1023K
V (Galactocentric GSR)	1237 ± 6 km/s	1991RC3.9.C...0000d
V (Local Group)	1197 ± 9 km/s	1996AJ....111..794K
V (3K CMB)	1638 ± 23 km/s	1996ApJ...473..576F
V (Virgo Infall only)	1552 ± 26 km/s	2000ApJ...529..786M
V (Virgo + GA only)	1694 ± 28 km/s	2000ApJ...529..786M
V (Virgo + GA + Shapley)	1705 ± 28 km/s	2000ApJ...529..786M

Hubble Flow Distance and Distance Modulus (where H₀ = 67.8 km/sec/Mpc ± km/sec/Mpc)

Type	Distance	Modulus
D (Galactocentric GSR)	18.25 ± 1.28 Mpc	(m-M) = 31.31 ± 0.15 mag
D (Local Group)	17.65 ± 1.24 Mpc	(m-M) = 31.23 ± 0.15 mag
D (3K CMB)	24.16 ± 1.73 Mpc	(m-M) = 31.92 ± 0.15 mag
D (Virgo Infall only)	22.90 ± 1.65 Mpc	(m-M) = 31.80 ± 0.15 mag
D (Virgo + GA only)	25.02 ± 1.76 Mpc	(m-M) = 31.99 ± 0.15 mag
D (Virgo + GA + Shapley)	25.15 ± 1.76 Mpc	(m-M) = 32.00 ± 0.15 mag

Scale at Hubble Flow Distances

Type	Values
Scale (Galactocentric GSR)	88 pc/arcsec = 0.088 kpc/arcsec = 5.31 kpc/arcmin = 0.32 Mpc/degree

2.3.3 Image 3
The display is longer than this page. Here is more:

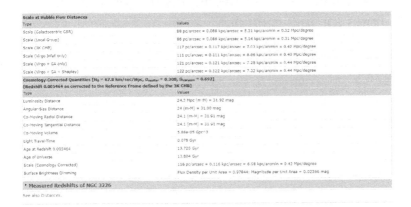

Scale at Hubble Flow Distances

Type	Values
Scale (Galactocentric GSR)	88 pc/arcsec = 0.088 kpc/arcsec = 5.31 kpc/arcmin = 0.32 Mpc/degree
Scale (Local Group)	86 pc/arcsec = 0.086 kpc/arcsec = 5.14 kpc/arcmin = 0.31 Mpc/degree
Scale (3K CMB)	117 pc/arcsec = 0.117 kpc/arcsec = 7.03 kpc/arcmin = 0.42 Mpc/degree
Scale (Virgo Infall only)	111 pc/arcsec = 0.111 kpc/arcsec = 6.66 kpc/arcmin = 0.40 Mpc/degree
Scale (Virgo + GA only)	121 pc/arcsec = 0.121 kpc/arcsec = 7.28 kpc/arcmin = 0.44 Mpc/degree
Scale (Virgo + GA + Shapley)	122 pc/arcsec = 0.122 kpc/arcsec = 7.32 kpc/arcmin = 0.44 Mpc/degree

Cosmology-Corrected Quantities [H_0 = 67.8 km/sec/Mpc, Ω_{matter} = 0.308, Ω_{vacuum} = 0.692]
[Redshift 0.005464 as corrected to the Reference Frame defined by the 3K CMB]

Type	Values
Luminosity Distance	24.3 Mpc (m-M) = 31.92 mag
Angular-Size Distance	24 (m-M) = 31.90 mag
Co-Moving Radial Distance	24.1 (m-M) = 31.91 mag
Co-Moving Tangential Distance	24.1 (m-M) = 31.91 mag
Co-Moving Volume	5.86e-05 Gpc^3
Light Travel-Time	0.078 Gyr
Age at Redshift 0.005464	13.726 Gyr
Age of Universe	13.804 Gyr
Scale (Cosmology Corrected)	116 pc/arcsec = 0.116 kpc/arcsec = 6.98 kpc/arcmin = 0.42 Mpc/degree
Surface Brightness Dimming	Flux Density per Unit Area = 0.97844; Magnitude per Unit Area = 0.02366 mag

▸ Measured Redshifts of NGC 3226

See also Distances.

2.3.4 Image 4
Selecting the Distances tab shows its data. The legend
indicates 11 lines for this galaxy.

Results for object NGC 3226

| Overview | Cross-IDs (46) | Coordinates (40) | Redshifts (26) | Distances (11) | Classifications (32) | Galactic Extinctions | Notes (16) | Diameters (11) |
| Photometry & SED (123) | Spectra (5) | Images (94) | References (378) | External Links | Survey Coverage | | | |

Redshift-independent Distances for NGC 3226

View References in ADS (6)

| (m-M) | err(m-M) | D(Mpc) | Method | Refcode | Notes | SN Name | Redshift | H0 | LMC Modulus |
double	double	double	char	char	char	char	double	double	double
31.86	0.14	23.60	SBF	2018AJ...146..86T				74.40	
31.86	0.24	23.60	SBF	2001ApJ...546..681T					
31.86	0.24	23.80	SBF	2001MNRAS.327.1004B					
37.89	0.24	23.80	SBF	2001MNRAS.327.1004B	Malmquist cor				
32.31	0.40	20.90	D-Sigma	1999ApJS..199.332N	Edist raw			75.05	
32.48	0.40	31.30	D-Sigma	1997ApJS..109.333W	Edist cor			75.00	
33.46	0.30	49.20	D-Sigma	1989ApJS..69.763F	Malmquist Corr			55.03	
33.68	0.25	59.90	D-Sigma	1989ApJS..69.763F	raw			50.00	
33.64	0.41	40.60	FP	2011MNRAS.327.1004B	Malmquist cor				
33.19	0.41	43.66	FP	2001MNRAS.327.1004B					
31.84	0.80	23.40	Tully est	1988NBGC.C..0P5T	B			75.00	

2.3.5 Image 5
Selecting the Spectra tab shows its data. The legend indicates 5 items for this galaxy.

2.3.6 Image 6
The display is longer than this page. Here is more of the display (second Optical with others below it):

FITS	N/A	Region:	Nucleus	Band:	Optical
Author ASCII	15.6kb	Telescope:	Palomar 200in	From:	6182.7 Å
MED ASCII	83.5kb	Instrument:	Double Spectrograph	To:	6827.8 Å
VOTable	79.0kb	Abs-Cal:	Yes	Step:	1.0 Å
		Ref-Frame:	Rest	Resolution:	2.5 Å
Reference:		Full description			
1995ApJS...98..477H					

FITS	N/A	Region:	Integrated	Line:	H I
Author ASCII	14.9kb	Telescope:	Nancay	From:	596.1 km s⁻¹
MED-ASCII	51.2kb	Instrument:	Auto-Correlator Spectrometer	To:	1823.3 km s⁻¹
VOTable	49.1kb	Abs-Cal:	Yes	Step:	1.1 km s⁻¹
		Ref-Frame:	Observed	Resolution:	7.9 km s⁻¹
Reference:		Full description			
2001A&A...379..379V					

FITS	N/A	Region:	Integrated	Line:	CO (1-0)
Author-ASCII	1.6kb	Telescope:	IRAM 30m	From:	625.6 km s⁻¹
MED-ASCII	3.1kb	Instrument:	SIS	To:	1955.2 km s⁻¹
VOTable	N/A	Abs-Cal:	Yes	Step:	21.2 km s⁻¹
		Ref-Frame:	Observed	Resolution:	5.0 km s⁻¹
Reference:		Full description			

There is a second CO line spectrum, not in the capture.

2.3.7 Image 7

The display is longer than this page. Here is more:

	FITS	N/A	Region:	Integrated	Line:	CO (1-0)
	Author-ASCII	1.6kb	Telescope:	IRAM 30m	From:	675.6 km s^{-1}
	NED-ASCII	3.1kb	Instrument:	SIS	To:	1955.2 km s^{-1}
PA = N/A	VOTable	N/A	Abs-Cal:	Yes	Step:	31.2 km s^{-1}
			Ref-Frame:	Observed	Resolution:	5.0 km s^{-1}
	Reference:		Full description			
	2011MNRAS.414..940					

	FITS	N/A	Region:	Integrated	Line:	CO (2-1)
	Author-ASCII	1.6kb	Telescope:	IRAM 30m	From:	675.6 km s^{-1}
	NED-ASCII	3.1kb	Instrument:	SIS	To:	1955.2 km s^{-1}
PA = N/A	VOTable	N/A	Abs-Cal:	Yes	Step:	31.2 km s^{-1}
			Ref-Frame:	Observed	Resolution:	5.0 km s^{-1}
	Reference:		Full description			
	2011MNRAS.414..940					

2.3.8 Image 8

There are 5 spectra for this galaxy. Here is only the first, making it clearer on this page. This is Optical from the Nucleus region, using the Palomar 200m Telescope and its Double Spectrograph Instrument.

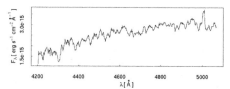

There is a metallic absorption line around 4300 A and a metallic emission line around 5000 A.

2.3.9 Image 9

Here is only the second spectrum of the 5.
This is Optical from the Nucleus region, using the
Palomar 200m Telescope and its Double Spectrograph
Instrument.

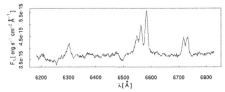

There are metallic emission lines around 6300 A, 6570,
and a pair around 6750 A.

2.3.10 Image 10

Here is only the third spectrum of the 5. This is the H I line from the Integrated Region using the Nancay Telescope and its Auto Correlator Spectrometer Instrument.

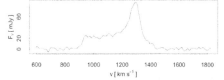

This is not a spectrum. Whatever spectrum was recorded, only a distribution of velocities is presented. This image offers no information of what was actually measured.

2.3.11 Image 11

Here is only the fourth spectrum of the 5. This is the CO (1-0) line from the Integrated region using the IRAM Telescope and its ISIS Instrument.

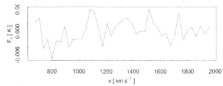

This is not a spectrum. Whatever spectrum was recorded, only a distribution of velocities is presented. This image offers no information of what was measured for CO.

2.3.12 Image 12

Here is only the last spectrum of the 5. This is the CO (2-1) line from the Integrated region using the IRAM Telescope and its ISIS Instrument.

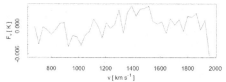

This is not a spectrum. Whatever spectrum was recorded, only a distribution of velocities is presented. NED offers no information of what was measured for CO.

—

2.3.13 NGC 3226 Data observations

There are several important observations with only one galaxy, which is serving as an example.

1) The redshift velocity value does not identify its origin. It is probably from one of the emission lines. This galaxy has several candidates in the first 2 spectra for a selection.

This is negligence, when providing a value without identifying its evidence.

2) The neutral hydrogen line measurement is not provided. Instead, only a velocity is plotted with a distribution of intensity across a range of velocities.

If such a measurement is being used as the galaxy redshift velocity, despite there being no value of a measured change in a wavelength, it requires explicit definition of its uncertainty and margin of error. This not a bell curve suggesting probabilities. This is closer to a random distribution of possible values, coming from a cloud of neutral hydrogen atoms moving independently toward a massive galaxy. Astronomers pick one the values from the disorganized set of atoms and assign it to the large body behind the cloud. This assignment is a mistake and cannot be justified.

2) The CO line measurements have no basis, like from a certain spectrogram. Instead, only a velocity set is charted with a distribution of intensity across a range of velocities.

I found nothing in the NED site or in Wikipedia explaining a CO line.

There are 2 measurements of CO line, but they have different distributions, while having the same range on the X-axis.

Whatever this CO line is, it must be ignored because it is physically impossible to measure the 3-dimensional velocity of a galaxy using a line of sight measurement of an emission line. To measure the proper velocity of a planet, many observations over a period of time are required. The same requirement applies to a galaxy.

3) Using CMB

There is a notable line on the Redshifts page:

[Redshift 0.005464 as corrected to the Reference Frame defined by the 3K CMB]

There is no Cosmic Microwave Background (this mistake is explained in section Big Bang), so any "correction" is actually a "corruption" so the redshift must have the correction removed. In any case, the redshift and spectrum are from atoms, and are not valid.

2.4 Galaxy Data from both references

This reference file in .xls format is compressed in a .zip format for convenient distribution.

Z-Galaxy-Data-WN.zip

The main worksheet, Galaxies, has over 1000 rows and over 70 columns. Compressing that content into a smaller page is impossible. [R36]

Many of the galaxies within our observable universe have a public position. Many, but not all, have a velocity (as km/s or z). Most of those also have a distance. Some have a size, measured in either light-years or arcseconds.

These data were compiled, when available, into this data set.

A diameter in lightyears is entered, and/or angular dimensions, depending on each galaxy's data. Sizes of galaxies are not used in this book, because I will not attempt to duplicate the algorithms which convert a magnitude and size into a luminosity and then to a distance.

The data are sorted in this order:

1) Sky quadrant, from NQ1 to SQ4,

2) Constellation by increasing Right Ascension,

3) Galaxy by increasing Right Ascension.

The Milky Way satellite galaxies are separated at the start of the list, as their close distances are unrelated to those of distant galaxies having nearby celestial coordinates.

The Magellanic Clouds are considered, in this data set, as Local Group galaxies. A study of groups of stars in both galaxies concluded their transverse velocity is too fast for them to be in orbit around the Milky Way. That conclusion takes them out of the list of Milky Way satellites which are assumed to be in orbit by gravity.

The most distant galaxies are at the end of the list, where they are sorted by coordinates. Most of them are in the distant background to nearer galaxies in the foreground. When all are sorted only by coordinates, then their correct relationship of foreground or background is not apparent.

The spreadsheet file has 2 worksheets:

1) Galaxies, with data for the over 600 galaxies and 24 Abell clusters.

Most of these clusters are very distant. To be included, the cluster must have a redshift value.

2) Cepheids, with the subset of 17 galaxies beyond our Local Group having a Cepheid.

The spreadsheet also has several charts, which are presented in this book.

The zip includes other files: 1) column definitions

2) TOC, which identifies by row number the respective quadrants in the long spreadsheet; this list is like a table of contents.

2.5 Constellation Data

Astronomers have defined a set of quadrants for the sky and assigned constellations to these quadrants.

I created a reference file for the constellations, including their abbreviation, and their quadrant and rough celestial coordinates.

The original was in Excel, but it is distributed in pdf. [R38]

Z-Constellations.pdf

3 Light

There are several interactions between light or electromagnetic radiation and atoms or matter.

3.1 Light and wavelengths

A spectrum is the entire range of wavelengths in electromagnetic radiation where light is the visible range. The ultraviolet and infrared ranges are not visible to the human eye but they are in the Sun's radiation. Because this radiation can come from sources spanning beyond the visible range and for simplicity, the word light is often used for the entire spectrum, including those frequency ranges not visible.

Electromagnetic radiation is the propagation of synchronized, perpendicular electric and magnetic fields. The propagation has a defined rate of oscillation measured as either a frequency or a wavelength. The wavelength is usually measured in either nanometers (10^{-9} m) or Angstroms (10^{-10} m or 0.1 nm). The velocity of this propagation has been measured in a vacuum using our standard definition for time and this measured value is called the constant c. This measurement also defined the standard unit of 1 meter. The velocity of propagation is reduced in a medium, defined by the medium's diffraction index.

Light transmits energy proportional to its frequency, so the constant c appears in some physics equations involving energy.

Quantum physics defined a theoretical particle called a photon to refer to a single wavelength.
In this section, wavelength is used because a spectrum analysis uses specific numerical values.
Using the word photon instead of wavelength only introduces possible confusion when the radiation is a continuum of energy having no discrete values. A rainbow is a continuum, not dots.

3.2 Synchrotron Radiation

Synchrotron radiation, electromagnetic energy emitted by charged particles (e.g., electrons and ions) that are moving at speeds close to that of light when their paths are altered, as by a magnetic field. It is so called because particles moving at such speeds in a variety of particle accelerator that is known as a synchrotron produce electromagnetic radiation of this sort.

Many kinds of astronomical objects have been found to emit synchrotron radiation as well. High-energy electrons spiraling through the lines of force of the magnetic field around the planet Jupiter, for example, give off synchrotron radiation at radio wavelengths. Synchrotron radiation at such wavelengths and at those of visible and ultraviolet light is generated by electrons moving in the magnetic field associated with the supernova remnant known as the Crab Nebula. Radio emissions of the synchrotron variety also have been detected from other supernova remnants in the Milky Way Galaxy and from extragalactic objects called quasars. [R41]

Observation:

There are many X-ray point sources in the universe including one at the core of most spiral galaxies. These sources were described in detail in the author's book Cosmology Transition.

As somewhat described in the excerpt above, all those X-ray sources have an electrical current whose path is bent by a magnetic field resulting in this broad spectrum of wavelengths spanning from X-ray to infrared.

Quasars are typically dimmed in the optical wavelengths by their surrounding clouds of gas and dust.

Note the source of synchrotron radiation is not an object in motion. The radiated energy originates from the point of interaction between an electric current and a magnetic field. This is not a mass in motion having kinetic energy.

It is impossible for the broad range of wavelengths in synchrotron radiation to be shifted by a Doppler Effect because the point of interaction is not a mass in motion.

As a simple comparison, a bolt of lightning is essentially a luminous electric current, often not in a linear path.

When this path changes its direction, between toward and away, in the line of sight to the observer, there is no Doppler effect on this light. The source is not a mass having kinetic energy which participates in the energy transfer from source to radiation by Doppler effect. Both lightning and synchrotron radiation are not generated by a body having mass and kinetic energy.

3.3 Thermal Radiation

Thermal radiation is electromagnetic radiation generated by the thermal motion of particles in matter. All matter with a temperature greater than absolute zero emits thermal radiation.

Emissivity must be defined before continuing.

The emissivity of the surface of a material is its effectiveness in emitting energy as thermal radiation. Thermal radiation is electromagnetic radiation that may include both visible radiation (light) and infrared radiation, which is not visible to human eyes. The thermal radiation from very hot objects (see photograph) is easily visible to the eye. Quantitatively, emissivity is the ratio of the thermal radiation from a surface to the radiation from an ideal black surface at the same temperature as given by the Stefan–Boltzmann law. The ratio varies from 0 to 1. The surface of a perfect black body (with an emissivity of 1) emits thermal radiation at the rate of approximately 448 watts per square metre at room temperature (25 °C, 298.15 K); all real objects have emissivities less than 1.0, and emit radiation at correspondingly lower rates. [R43]

If a radiation object meets the physical characteristics of a black body in thermodynamic equilibrium, the radiation is called blackbody radiation. Planck's law describes the spectrum of blackbody radiation, which depends solely on the object's temperature. Wien's displacement law determines the most likely frequency of the emitted radiation, and the Stefan–Boltzmann law gives the radiant intensity for the wavelength. [R43]

Observation:

Thermal radiation is also one of the fundamental mechanisms of heat transfer. Conduction between adjacent solid objects is another.

Its spectrum is characterized by a wavelength distribution, with the wavelength having the highest intensity related to the object's temperature.

The wavelength distribution affects whether it is visible. A cool temperature won't be. When warmer the increasing infrared intensity can be felt as heat or warmth but not seen. A rising temperature will become visible as red. When even hotter the mix of color wavelengths can result in "white hot." Our Sun is hot enough to generate the ultraviolet frequency which is not visible but can affect the eyes and skin.

Our white Sun can appear yellow when overhead due to the wavelength distribution after the light passes through our atmosphere, with the yellow wavelength having the strongest intensity. The atmosphere can also cause a color change between sun rise and sun set, toward red, and it causes the sky to be blue.

Here is the thermal radiation spectrum from our Sun: [R44]

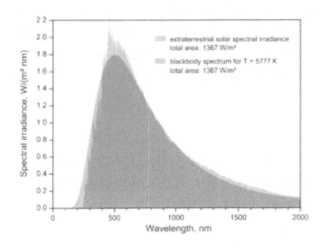

My observation about wavelengths:

Thermal radiation typically spans a continuum of energy from ultraviolet to infrared with wavelengths covering most temperatures.

Infrared is always present but shorter wavelengths arise only with a very high surface temperature. Our Sun's thermal radiation, seen as light, is in this wavelength range of UV to infrared.

Most emission lines from atoms range from visible to ultraviolet wavelengths. As a rule, any wavelengths measured outside of this range, like radio at the low end, and X-ray or gamma ray at the high end, were emitted by a source of synchrotron radiation, not thermal.

A fictitious black hole violates this rule because its impossible hot accretion disk is claimed to emit X-rays but that energy requires an impossible temperature.

Thermal radiation requires a surface, like found in a liquid or solid, or condensed matter, meaning not a gas.

The temperature of a gas is measured by the kinetic energy of its atoms or molecules. A gas cannot emit thermal radiation. When its atoms and molecules become ionized, then as each ion captures an electron, they emit their characteristic wavelength of electromagnetic radiation. This is the non-thermal mechanism for the color of a neon light.

3.4 Fraunhofer Lines

This description provides background for several terms and their use in a spectrum analysis.

In 1814, Fraunhofer independently rediscovered the [dark] lines and began to systematically study and measure the wavelengths where these features are observed. He mapped over 570 lines.

About 45 years later Kirchhoff and Bunsen noticed that several Fraunhofer lines coincide with characteristic emission lines identified in the spectra of heated elements. It was correctly deduced that dark lines in the solar spectrum are caused by absorption by chemical elements in the solar atmosphere. Some of the observed features were identified as telluric lines originating from absorption by oxygen molecules in the Earth's atmosphere.

Because of their well–defined wavelengths, Fraunhofer lines are often used to characterize the refractive index and dispersion properties of optical materials. [R47]

3.5 Atom's characteristic wavelengths

3.5.1 Calcium

M31 or Andromeda galaxy is an example of the calcium atom in a galaxy spectrum.

The M31 spectrum has the calcium ion's pair of calcium absorption lines at 3934 and 3969 Angstroms in its spectrum. They are from calcium ions in the line of sight to the galaxy. A red or blue shift of this pair of lines indicates the relative velocity of the ion. The neutral calcium atom has a different pair of wavelengths.
Nearly all matter in the universe is plasma, or it has an electrical charge. That includes electrons (-), protons (+), and ions (+) which are atoms having lost one or more electrons.

Hydrogen is the most common element in the universe; it is also the simplest having only one proton and one electron.

Other elements, beyond hydrogen and calcium, including carbon, nitrogen and oxygen are found in some galaxies. In cosmology, a metallic element is any other than hydrogen and helium. In chemistry, some elements are called metals because of their behaviors in chemical reactions. In this case of astronomical data and measurements, chemistry's use of the term must be ignored. In astronomy, all but 2 elements, H and He, of the 118, are metals.

When metals are observed in a galaxy, the specific elements can be inconsistent. One galaxy might have C, N, and O, while another might not have C. The specific mix is useful only for research. Atoms cannot indicate a galaxy's velocity.

3.6 Lyman-alpha line

In physics, the Lyman-alpha line is a spectral line of hydrogen, or more generally of one-electron ions, in the Lyman series, emitted when the electron falls from the n = 2 orbital to the n = 1 orbital, where n is the principal quantum number. In hydrogen, its wavelength of 1215.67 angstroms corresponding to frequency of 10^{15} hertz, places the Lyman-alpha line in the ultraviolet part of the electromagnetic spectrum, which is absorbed by air. Lyman-alpha astronomy must therefore ordinarily be carried out by satellite-borne instruments, except for extremely distant sources whose red shifts allow the hydrogen line to penetrate the atmosphere. [R48]

Observation:

This wavelength is important because a quasar usually has this emission line in its spectrum.
A shift of this emission line wavelength indicates the relative velocity of the atom, not the quasar or galaxy.

3.7 Neutral Hydrogen line

This line might be observed with many galaxies.

The hydrogen line, 21-centimeter line, or H I line is the electromagnetic radiation spectral line that is created by a change in the energy state of neutral hydrogen atoms.

This electromagnetic radiation is at the precise frequency of 1,420,405,751.7667±0.0009 Hz, which is equivalent to the vacuum wavelength of 21.1061140542 cm in free space. This wavelength falls within the microwave region of the electromagnetic spectrum, and it is observed frequently in radio astronomy because those radio waves can penetrate the large clouds of interstellar cosmic dust that are opaque to visible light. [R49]

Observation:
It is possible for neutral hydrogen atoms to be found anywhere. If the emission line is shifted, then the atom must be in motion. The neutral atom could be in motion for 2 reasons:
1) The force of gravity from another mass is pulling the neutral atom in that direction, or
2) The proton was in motion by the Coulomb's force between charges when it captured an electron becoming a neutral hydrogen atom.

When this line is observed in the spectrum of a distant galaxy it is always red shifted. That redshift suggests the neutral atom is moving toward the massive galaxy, away from the observer, here on or near Earth. Gravity explains that motion. The red shift of these atoms moving away Earth and toward another galaxy cannot be assumed to be the other galaxy's velocity.

3.8 NIST Reference

NIST has a web page to view the lines associated with each element if any values are needed. [R50]

4 Doppler Effect

The Doppler Effect is a critical observation in cosmology.

Here is one definition:

Doppler effect, the apparent difference between the frequency at which sound or light waves leave a source and that at which they reach an observer, caused by relative motion of the observer and the wave source. This phenomenon is used in astronomical measurements. [R51]

Observation:

Light and sound are similar when the velocity of the source cannot affect the velocity of the light or sound being propagated. The velocities of light and sound are always defined by the medium. A moving source affects only the frequency of the wave or oscillation, not the velocity of propagation.
The Doppler Effect with light is observed when the entire spectrum of the light source has shifted in proportion to the light source's velocity in that direction. The velocity of light cannot be affected by the light source velocity. However, the source in motion affects the distribution around the sphere of the radiated energy, never its velocity.

The timing of the Doppler Effect is crucial when one observes a spectrum shift in radiation from distant objects.

The Doppler Effect occurs only at the moment of radiation emission, when the motion of the object at that instant affects the spectrum.

There are 2 sources of electromagnetic radiation affected by the Doppler Effect: stars and atoms.

Stars emit thermal radiation, where the distribution of energy across its range of wavelengths is related to the temperature of the heat source. Stars emit their energy in the range of thermal from ultraviolet to infrared, so an eye is sensitive to part of that range in what is called visible light.

An ion emits a characteristic wavelength, when capturing an electron and the atom becomes neutral. If the ion is in motion, its kinetic energy participates in the energy transfer, observed as a shift in the wavelength proportional to the ion's velocity relative to the velocity of light.

Similarly, an atom or ion can absorb a characteristic wavelength, when transferring energy to its electrons, or to its internal energy state. If the atom or ion is in motion, its kinetic energy participates in the energy transfer, observed as a shift in the absorption line's wavelength proportional to the atom's velocity relative to the velocity of light.

The star's thermal radiation or an atom's emission line initiates the propagation of the synchronized electric and magnetic fields. This propagation is an expanding sphere from the source. This sphere of energy continues until it is absorbed by an object in its path.

Stars emit a broad spectrum of thermal radiation. The energy distribution among the wavelengths is driven by the object's temperature, which a measurement of the internal molecular vibrations. The nuclei are electrical charges in motion, though within a very small range.

Atoms emit or absorb a characteristic wavelength based on the electron configuration.

The energy change in the atom is transferred to the corresponding wavelengths of electromagnetic radiation. Some atoms emit more than one wavelength when dropping to their ground state.

These wavelengths can be observed and measured in a spectrum and are called emission lines.

The instant of radiation emission, the motion of the source affects the wavelength distribution around that sphere. Wavelengths in the direction of the source are changed by an amount proportional to the source's velocity relative to the velocity of light. The light source is generating a continuum of energy as a sphere. Wavelengths in one side of the sphere will be reduced, or toward the blue end, in the direction of the source. Wavelengths in the other side of the sphere will be increased, or toward the red end, in the direction opposite of the source. There is perfect symmetry with the change in wavelength on one side exactly matched by the change on the opposite side. The sphere is a continuum of energy, being carried in wavelengths. There is no quantized behavior present.

The motion of the light source does not change the amount of energy being radiated, but only its distribution around the sphere of its propagation. Energy is always conserved.

The Doppler Effect also occurs only at the moment of radiation absorption by an atom, when the motion of the atom at that instant also affects the spectrum. When energy is absorbed by an atom than that energy is missing from the radiation, observed by a line missing from the continuum. The energy is carried in wavelengths so those wavelengths carrying the energy which was transferred to the object are missing in the spectrum from the light source. These missing wavelengths are called absorption lines.

Absorption lines arise from atoms in the line of sight, between the light source which emits the intact energy or spectrum.

The absorption line behavior is affected by the velocity of the atom. A moving atom carries kinetic energy, and that energy participates in the transfer of energy from the radiation to the atom. As with an emission line, the velocity of the atom relative to the velocity of light determines the amount of energy involved in the exchange.

An atom is essentially a tiny sphere. An atom in the path of electromagnetic radiation can absorb energy from that continuum of energy. The atom's motion relative to the radiation is important. The motion at that point in the sphere will have a proportion relative to the velocity of light and relative to the direction of the incoming light.

When the atom is moving toward the light source the kinetic energy of the atom is a participant and it reduces the energy the atom requires for a state change and absorbs from the radiation. A decrease in energy is a higher wavelength.

Energy is always conserved during this exchange.

When the atom is moving away from the light source the kinetic energy of the atom is a participant and it increases the energy the atom requires and absorbs from the radiation. This increase in energy is a lower wavelength.
The energy being absorbed is noted as an absorption line wavelength.

4.1 Doppler Calculations

This is the simple calculation of z.

The velocity, called v here, of the source is compared to the velocity of light by dividing that value by the velocity of light, called the constant c.

The value of v has a sign. Doppler Effect is in the observer's line of sight. When the object is moving away from the observer, v is + or positive, and when moving toward the observer, v is – or negative.

The result is called z by convention.

The simple equation is $z=v/c$, making sure the units are the same (usually km/s).

The shift in a spectrum due to the motion of the light
source is a simple equation,
where EWL is the emission wavelength,

NWL is the new wavelength, so:
NWL = EWL + (EWL multiplied by z)

where the z is the factor for the change in the new
wavelength from that originally emitted; z is positive for
a red shift or negative for a blue shift.

There is no quantized behavior in any of the equation's
factors or in the result.

4.2 Galaxy Red Shift

The Local Group has 2 galaxies, M31 and M33, with
blue shifts. The spectrum of galaxies beyond our Local
Group exhibit a unique behavior. In 1936, Edwin
Hubble noticed this and put our Local Group on an
island separate from the Hubble Flow.

These galaxies have a lyman-alpha emission line
which shifts toward the red, and in the limited data set
of galaxies measured before 1926 this shift increases
as the galaxy's distance increases from the observer,
who is always on or near the Earth.

As the atoms are neutral, they will be pulled by gravity
toward the nearest galaxy having the most mass.
Depending on their initial distance the sustained
acceleration can reach a higher velocity.
Motion toward another galaxy is away from Earth, so
the atom has a redshift.
Improving imaging technology enables a spectrum to
be captured from galaxies which had been too dim by

their distance. The dim, distant galaxies often exhibited a lyman-alpha emission line.

All share the same red shifted Lyman-alpha emission line.

These galaxies have this line with a red shift indicating the atom is moving at many multiples of the speed of light, like 7x. A proton when capturing an electron emits this characteristic wavelength. The wavelength is shifted by the proton's velocity at the instant of that capture. This redshift comes from the new hydrogen atom in the line of sight and indicates nothing about the distant galaxy's actual motion.

Also, a galaxy's lyman-alpha red shift of $z > 1$ indicates a proton's velocity is exceeding that of light. Einstein developed the theory of relativity assuming mass cannot travel faster than c. His unjustified assumption was shown to be a mistake several galaxies. Relativity has too many mistakes.

By mistake, this hydrogen emission line redshift was considered the result of a velocity of another object causing a Doppler effect. This is only a line of sight behavior, and any atom's emission line indicates nothing about the distant galaxy's actual velocity. This mistake caused many others, including the universe expansion, dark energy, and the Big Bang.

Essentially, the only limit on a galaxy redshift is the technology to measure the most distant ones. Treating this z as a velocity of the galaxy is ridiculous. Scientists eventually tried to explain how galaxies could possibly have a velocity exceeding 8x the velocity of light by an expanding fabric of space.

4.3 Quasar Red Shift

A quasar is a distant object which looks like a star, but it has a strong source of synchrotron radiation, extending from radio to X-ray. Many quasars were found by their radio emissions. All quasars share redshifted emission lines from a variety of non-hydrogen elements where the mix can vary by quasar.

These quasars can also have this lyman-alpha line with a red shift indicating the atom is moving at many multiples of the speed of light, like 7x. A proton when capturing an electron emits this characteristic wavelength. The wavelength is shifted by the proton's velocity at the instant of that capture. This red shift comes from the atom in the line of sight, and indicates nothing about the distant quasar's actual motion. This mistake compounds the galaxy red shift mistake, so both objects have a different mechanism. This makes the false dark energy difficult to explain both false velocities. Therefore, a quasar usually has 2 measurable redshifts. 1st from the metallic ion emission lines. 2nd from the Lyman-alpha emission line. The 1st always has a lower z (< 1) than the 2nd, at z > 1.

Also, a quasar's hydrogen red shift of z > 1 indicates a proton's velocity is exceeding that of light. Einstein developed the theory of relativity assuming mass cannot travel faster than c. His unjustified assumption was shown to be a mistake by many quasars. Relativity has too many mistakes.

Halton Arp in his work with quasars failed to recognize a quasar has 2 red shifts. His book Seeing Red, even has 2 spectrograms illustrating that dual behavior, but Arp always used 1 of the 2 z values, the lower, in his descriptions. This was not deception. In some interviews, he indicates someone else measured the redshift. Also, as z increases, the emission line shifts further toward infrared where it might not be seen. If the spectrogram cuts off longer wavelengths like in infrared, the high redshifted line might be lost as a result.

Clearly, Arp was unaware of the mechanisms being measured for the values of galaxy and quasar, and it appears others gave him the redshift value rather personally calculating it. He catalogued his observations without having to do the calculations. If Arp was aware of 2 red shifts his book would have reached different conclusions. Arp is noted for his extensive observations including his well-known compilation of peculiar galaxies.

Many others do not understand the redshift mechanisms. I cannot know for sure, but perhaps I was the first to declare quasars have 2 redshifts, one from Lyman-alpha and a second from the metallic ions. I posted "Arp's Misleading Quasar Sample" on May 20, 2020. Before this post, I noticed in Arp's book Seeing Red has spectrograms of two associated quasars, so I analyzed them. I found for both the Lyman-alpha line is shifted far into the infrared, near the right-side edge. I suspect Arp never knew his book shows quasars having 2 distinct measurable redshifts. [R59]

For those interested in more details about quasars, they are in my earlier books like Cosmology

Connections. This book is about measuring velocities. The minimum description should be enough for here.

An annotated quasar spectrum, from Caltech, is included in the section Quasars.

4.4 Redshift summary

The term "redshift" is used so loosely, most think of it as just a simple number having a consistent meaning, like a temperature.

A redshift is not that simple and anyone using the term so loosely is showing they consider it as just a simple number.

It is crucial to recognize there are at least 5 different redshifts. Each is a measurement of a distinct behavior.

Galaxies are totally different entities than quasars. A galaxy has billions of stars while a quasar is a quasi-stellar object having no stars.

A quasar's red shift can come from only emission lines from ions capturing electrons. None of these emission lines indicate anything about the quasar.

Similarly, a galaxy's measured red or blue shift can only be in absorption or emission lines from atoms in the line of sight. Each shift is measured as a change, and the result of a ratio is a dimensionless value called z. It is a mistake to call this measurement using atoms as a velocity of the object behind them.

As noted earlier, a metallic element is one which is not hydrogen or helium.

The 5 distinct red shifts are:

1) Galaxy – hydrogen absorption (several)

2) Galaxy – hydrogen emission lines (several)

3) Galaxy – metal

4) Quasar – hydrogen emission lines (several)

5) Quasar – metal

Shift (1): There are several series of hydrogen absorption lines. The single electron orbiting the single proton can take 1 of many orbits, or energy states. The first 2 sets have been defined as the Lyman and Balmer series; there are more series. The Lyman-alpha absorption line is at 1216 Angstroms. Any absorption lines must be from atoms in the line of sight and are not from the galaxy. This book will ignore other hydrogen lines, like from the Balmer series.
 The hydrogen absorption lines are never observed in the spectrum of a galaxy, only the emission lines from those series.

Shift (2): There are at least 2 hydrogen emission lines, the Lyman-alpha line at 1216 Angstroms, and the neutral hydrogen line at 21 cm. Both lines must be from atoms in the line of sight and are not from the galaxy. This book will ignore other series of hydrogen lines, like Balmer.

Shift (3): A notable example of a metallic line is the blue shift in M31, Andromeda galaxy. The calcium ion absorption line is driven by calcium ions near the galactic corona. Calcium is a metal. The metallic emission line originates in the ion but not in the primary light source, the galaxy. Software analysis of M31 spectrum can find the lyman-alpha emission line, so M31 does capture a proton. The pair of calcium absorption lines are so obvious, they are used. The 2 spectrograms of M31 are shown in section Galaxies, where M31 and M33 are the first 2 examples.

Shift (4): The quasar high red shift comes from the hydrogen Lyman-alpha emission line. It is possible the highest redshift comes from the Balmer-alpha emission line when the captured electron has less velocity than for a capture emitting the Lyman-alpha line. The Balmer series lines appear less often in quasars than the Lyman series.

Shift (5): The quasar low red shift comes from the metallic ion emission lines.

Shift (1): This line can never be a galaxy velocity.

Shift (2): There are galaxies with either a red or blue shift of the metallic ion absorption lines. M31 has a calcium line blue shifted. This can never be a galaxy velocity, nor can it be related to a galaxy distance. Only a Cepheid provides a distance metric.

LINER galaxies, which include Seyferts, exhibit several metallic elements when taking the spectrum of their AGN. None of these metallic lines in a LINER galaxy spectrum are related to the galaxy's motion.

Shift (4): The hydrogen Lyman-alpha emission line is found in a "typical" quasar. This can never be a quasar velocity, nor can it be related to a quasar distance.

Shift (5): These metallic lines are found in the quasars used by Halton Arp, in his book Seeing Red. This red shift can never be a quasar velocity, nor can it be related to a quasar distance, nor can it be related to the age of matter. These ions just slow down in apparent incremental changes in their velocity.

The z value for (4) has exceeded 7, while the z value for (5) is < 1.

It is crucial to note that none of the 5 types of a red shift is an indicator of the object's real velocity.
None of the redshifts have a useful application.

All 4 types are defined to prevent a wrong application, like a velocity of another object.

No redshift is a velocity, except with an atom or star. Galaxies and quasars are neither.
When one accepts that simple fact about the false velocities, then there is no "Hubble Flow." That was the term Edwin Hubble used initially for the redshift trend.

Dark energy arose from the wrong assumption that the false expansion is consistent.

There is no expansion, no dark energy, and no big bang.

4.5 Atoms and Stars

Atoms and stars are not in the list with galaxies and quasars.

An atom generating an emission line is a light source so its motion results in a true Doppler effect.

Similarly, an atom absorbing its characteristic wavelength has its kinetic energy participate in the energy transfer so its motion results in a true Doppler effect for its absorption line.

A star's photosphere is a light source, so the star's motion results in a true Doppler effect on its light. A Star and its planets rotate around the system's center of gravity. This shift of the star's entire spectrum can be measured. Most exoplanets are found by their blocking some of the light from their star, when their orbit takes them in the line of sight.
Some exoplanets are found using what is called the wobble method. The cycle of a star's wobble with its planets results in a cycle of red and blue shifts. An analysis of this cycle, using Kepler's laws of planetary

motion, enables finding the mass and orbits of the respective exoplanets.

Astronomers made a mistake when interpreting the alternating spectrum of variable stars, seeing it as a Doppler effect (kappa mechanism), not as a temperature change. A star's light is thermal radiation, so its wavelength distribution is driven by its photosphere temperature. That is how the temperature of every star is measured.

Variable stars are noted for their measured luminosity cycle having a peak followed by several days before the peak repeats.

Pierre-Marie Robitaille's LMH model of the Sun or stars, offers a better explanation for all observed stellar behaviors than cosmology offers. His model was mentioned in the section Stars.

4.6 Cosmological Red Shift

Cosmological redshift is the result of failing to understand the mechanism driving a measured red shift.
   One mistake with absorption and emission lines is treating them as a velocity. These lines are behaviors only in the line of sight and are not within the distant object

Cosmological red shift simply ignores the mechanisms driving a change in an object's spectrum.

This is one explanation:

Laboratory experiments here on Earth have determined that each element in the periodic table emits photons only at certain wavelengths (determined by the excitation state of the atoms). These photons are manifest as either emission or absorption lines in the spectrum of an astronomical object, and by measuring the position of these spectral lines, we can determine which elements are present in the object itself or along the line of sight. However, when astronomers perform this analysis, they note that for most astronomical objects, the observed spectral lines are all shifted to longer (redder) wavelengths. This is known as 'cosmological redshift' (or more commonly just 'redshift'). [R67]

Observation:

There is a very big mistake in this description.
The phrase "the observed spectral lines are all shifted to longer wavelengths" is wrong.

With most galaxies, there is only 1 emission line being affected. It is either the neutral hydrogen line or the Lyman-alpha line. "All lines" is definitely wrong when every observation finds only one.

In a proposed cosmological redshift, all wavelengths from the source are lengthened as the light travels through (supposedly expanding) space. Cosmological redshift results from the expansion of space itself and not from the motion of an individual body.

The galaxy spectrum at its source has no absorption or emission lines. All lines originate in the line of sight. They should never be used for the galaxy's velocity. This was explained in section Star vs Galaxy.

This cosmological redshift is a big mistake by ignoring how red shifts are measured.

Cosmological redshift violates the conservation of energy.

The reason is with the Doppler Effect at the moment of emission or absorption, light does not gain or lose energy through the event. The Doppler Effect is either a transfer of energy or a change in its distribution within the sphere radiating from the source.

A blue shift or red shift at any other time is a change in the radiation energy with no identified partner for a transfer. This is a violation of conservation of energy. A red shift is a loss of energy. A blue shift is a gain of energy.

A red shift of all wavelengths is a loss of energy. This cannot happen. This cosmological redshift is a mistake of confusion, when trying to solve the redshift mistake.

5 Stars

The internal mechanism driving a star's thermal radiation is not relevant to this book. However, I must mention the current gaseous Sun model is being questioned. Later, there are assumptions based on the old model of a star; these must be questioned.

A new solar model as building blocks of LMH was also explained in my book Cosmology Transition. I referenced several links or Robitaille's pages.[R69]

Briefly, Dr. Pierre-Marie Robitaille developed a solar model based on condensed matter in the form of liquid metallic hydrogen. This is the term for a lattice of protons maintained by loose electrons. This lattice is electrically conductive and cools by emitting thermal radiation. This model explains all solar and stellar observations. He has presented this model in many venues including his YouTube channel, Sky Scholar which hosts many videos. [R70] There are increasing numbers of scientists receptive to this solar LMH model. The current gaseous solar Model powered by fusion in its core fails to explain many observations. It persists despite those conflicts. Among the failures of the fusion model:

a) The mechanism for the observed thermal spectrum,
b) The internal distinct layers measured by helio-seismology,
c) The different rates of rotation by latitude of its perfect sphere,
d) Limb darkening,
e) The various events on the photosphere's liquid surface,
f) The mechanism for the solar wind.

All are explained by the model using condensed matter in the form of liquid metallic hydrogen which is a lattice of protons maintained by loose electrons. This lattice is electrically conductive, so it supports the observed electromagnetic phenomena, like sunspots.

One of the significant conclusions from the different efforts researching the mechanisms in the Sun is new elements are being created on the surface of the photosphere by the process of transmutation. This is not the improbable mechanism of impossible pressures and temperatures which are required to sustain fusion of atomic nuclei for billions of years. Nearly all elements in the periodic table are found in the solar spectrum so they must be either on or very near the photosphere. They are being created in that complex electromagnetic environment capable of a great force of compression. This is not the ideal gas environment in an enclosed volume where pressure and temperature become related. No star possesses such a container.

The current star types are defined primarily by the measured surface temperature. That is how the Sun gets its assigned type. However, many types also reference the presence of specific elements in their spectrum. These elements are assumed to be present by the stage of the star's internal fusion cycle.

Now that the solar model is changing from internal fusion to surface transmutation, all assumptions based on the distribution of elements in a star's spectrum lose their validity. The ratio of elements is called metallicity and is used to draw conclusions on the age of collections of stars, like in galaxies or globular clusters. The result of these assumptions becoming invalid affects the many analyses in cosmology based on them.

This book is about measuring velocities, not stars, but some stars have a role in the process.

Changing the mechanisms in a star is a paradigm shift in cosmology.

This book assumes a star has a photosphere having a physical liquid surface based on liquid metallic hydrogen, as described by Robitaille.

This book will reference only the 2 variable star types, Cepheid or RR Lyrae. Other types are less important to galaxies in general, though of course, most galaxies have a mix of star types.

These variable stars are among the brightest so their magnitude can be measured by telescopes having the necessary resolution.

There are other bright, giant stars, but the variable stars are much easier to identify in a series of images.

5.1 Cepheid

Cepheid is the most frequently used type of variable star.

A Cepheid variable is a type of star that changes in brightness with a well-defined stable period and amplitude.
A strong direct relationship between a Cepheid variable's luminosity and pulsation period established Cepheids as important indicators of cosmic benchmarks for scaling galactic and extragalactic distances.

This robust characteristic of classical Cepheids was discovered in 1908 by Henrietta Swan Leavitt after studying thousands of variable stars in the Magellanic Clouds.

This discovery allows one to know the true luminosity of a Cepheid by simply observing its pulsation period. This in turn allows one to determine the distance to the star, by comparing its known luminosity to its observed brightness.

The term Cepheid originates from Delta Cephei in the constellation Cepheus, identified by John Goodricke in 1784, the first of its type to be so identified. Chief among the uncertainties tied to the classical and type II Cepheid distance scale are: the nature of the period-luminosity relation in various passbands, the impact of metallicity on both the zero-point and slope of those relations, and the effects of photometric contamination (blending) and a changing (typically unknown) extinction law on Cepheid distances. All these topics are actively debated in the literature.

These unresolved matters have resulted in cited values for the Hubble constant (established from Classical Cepheids) ranging between 60 km/s/Mpc and 80 km/s/Mpc. Resolving this discrepancy is one of the foremost problems in astronomy since the cosmological parameters of the Universe may be constrained by supplying a precise value of the Hubble constant.

Delta Cephei is also of particular importance as a calibrator of the Cepheid period-luminosity relation since its distance is among the most precisely established for a Cepheid, partly because it is a member of a star cluster and the availability of precise Hubble Space Telescope / Hipparcos parallaxes. The accuracy of the distance measurements to Cepheid variables and other bodies within 7,500 lightyears is vastly improved by combining images from Hubble taken six months apart when the Earth and Hubble are on opposite sides of the Sun.

As detected thus far, NGC 3370, a spiral galaxy in the constellation Leo, contains the farthest Cepheids yet found at a distance of 29 Mpc. Cepheid variable stars are in no way perfect distance markers: at nearby galaxies they have an error of about 7% and up to a 15% error for the most distant. [R73]

Observation:

The Cepheid has known limitations, but for a long time a variable star having a consistent luminosity curve was the only reliable method to determine a particular galaxy's distance, its host. Alternate methods have been developed in recent decades. Individual sections in this book will cover several of them.

The 7 to 15% error is very important. References for research, should indicate such details. When a distance comes from an average, the value lacking that detail implies precision, when there was none.

This practice can be inconsistent in Wikipedia. Its topics for the elements will sometimes include the % of each isotope to know exactly where the final value came from. Lacking those percentages could imply all the atoms of this element have the same atomic mass, which is wrong.

If the distance to a galaxy is the result of combining more than one possibility, then the value must also note this result which hides the real data.

For example, if the value is the average of two, ignoring the two values and providing only the average is quite misleading about the value's precision.

5.2   RR Lyrae

RR Lyrae is a type of variable star, like a Cepheid, but used less often.

RR Lyrae is a variable star in the Lyra constellation, figuring in its west near to Cygnus. As the brightest star in its class, it became the eponym for the RR Lyrae variable class of stars and it has been extensively studied by astronomers. RR Lyrae variables serve as important standard candles that are used to measure astronomical distances. The period of pulsation of an RR Lyrae variable depends on its mass, luminosity and temperature, while the difference between the measured luminosity and the actual luminosity allows its distance to be determined via the inverse-square law. Hence, understanding the period-luminosity relation for a local set of such stars allows the distance of more distant stars of this type to be determined.

The distance of RR Lyrae remained uncertain until 2002 when the Hubble Space Telescope's fine guidance sensor was used to determine the distance of RR Lyrae within a 5% margin of error, yielding a value of 262 parsecs (855 light-years). When combined with measurements from the Hipparcos satellite and other sources, the result is a distance estimate of 258 pc (841 ly). [R74]

Observation:

Using the RR Lyrae has known limitations, including a shorter usable distance range compared to the Cepheid.

Alternate methods for a distance calculation have been developed in recent decades. They are described in section NED distances.

6 Star vs Galaxy

An astronomer in France captured the spectra of M31 and 3 stars on one web page, titled "The Radial Velocity Measure of nearby galaxies" [R76]

The spectrum of M31 galaxy is at the left while and 3 stars of different types are at the right.

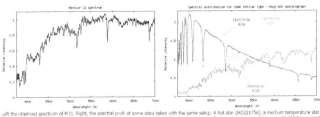

Left the observed spectrum of M31. Right, the spectral profil of some stars taken with the same setup. A hot star (HD221756), a medium temperature star ?5239, spectrum similar to Sun) and a relatively cool star, Aldebaran (alpha Tau). The Messier 31 central region spectrum match more with Aldebaran spectrum. Clearly, this part of the galaxy contain red cool objects (stellar population I).

The M31 spectrum has the distinctive relatively flat intensities with erratic fluctuations spanning from ultraviolet at the left to infrared at the right.

Any big dips are absorption lines from atoms in the line of sight to the galaxy.

There are 2 close absorption lines just below 4000A. This pair is from a calcium ion. They are slightly blue shifted indicating a velocity of -300 km/s. This is the velocity incorrectly assigned to M31. These calcium ions have the same velocity as ions in the slow solar wind. The massive M31 is not moving at the same velocity as particles in the slow solar wind. Absorption and emission lines in a galaxy spectrum must be ignored, to avoid a wrong velocity for the galaxy.

The 3 stars have different colors. All are emitting thermal radiation which has a wavelength distribution defined by the temperature of the surface which is transferring some of its thermal energy to electromagnetic radiation, in the form of thermal radiation.

Blue is the hot, type A1 star. Note its highest intensity wavelength is at the far left, at about 4000A, in ultraviolet.

Green is the temperate type G2V star which is like our Sun. Note its highest intensity wavelength is around 6000A or yellow, in visible. This star will look white as the intensity of all the visible colors are the same. The human eye will se the mix of wavelengths as white.

Red is the cool, type K5 star, Aldebaran, or a red giant. Note its highest intensity wavelength is at the right, at about 7000A, or the color red. The figure cut off above 7000A, with the infrared wavelengths.

Note that all 3 stars have some absorption lines in their spectrum. These atoms must be attached to the photosphere. If a star is moving in the line of sight to Earth, then by the Doppler effect the entire spectrum would shift to the left (shorter wavelengths) when moving toward Earth, or to the right (longer wavelengths) when moving away.

The astronomer can inspect the absorption lines, identify their elements, calculate the z value from the ratio of change to nominal wavelength, multiply z time c to get a velocity of the atoms on the photosphere. While attached, they have a common velocity.

A galaxy has no external light-emitting surface like a photosphere for atoms attaching, so all atoms in the line of sight to a galaxy are never attached and can never have a common velocity.

When looking at the spectra on the earlier page, they look similar.

The astronomer must remember the lines with a star can be measured, but the lines with a galaxy must be ignored.

Since cosmology is in a crisis by wrong velocities, clearly, for over 100 years, astronomers were never told this simple rule for galaxies.

The same rule applies to quasars. The section Quasars has the sp0ectrum of a typical quasar. It has many emission lines, coming from different elements. A quasar has no external surface for atoms attaching. All lines with a quasar must be ignored because none share a velocity with the quasar.

Astronomers must remember the rules for measuring the velocity of a star CANNOT be used for a galaxy or quasar.

When having no outer light-emitting surface, it is impossible for a galaxy or quasar to reveal its velocity by atoms in its spectrum.

7 Galaxies

The Data Set containing galaxy data identifies the type of every galaxy in the list.

7.1 Definition of the types

Wikipedia offers a detailed explanation of them.

An excerpt from Galaxy morphological classification:

Galaxy morphological classification is a system used by astronomers to divide galaxies into groups based on their visual appearance. There are several schemes in use by which galaxies can be classified according to their morphologies, the most famous being the Hubble sequence, devised by Edwin Hubble and later expanded by Gérard de Vaucouleurs and Allan Sandage. However, galaxy classification and morphology are now largely done using computational methods and physical morphology.

The de Vaucouleurs system retains Hubble's basic division of galaxies into ellipticals, lenticulars, spirals and irregulars. To complement Hubble's scheme, de Vaucouleurs introduced a more elaborate classification system for spiral galaxies, based on three morphological characteristics:
Bars. Galaxies are divided on the basis of the presence or absence of a nuclear bar. De Vaucouleurs introduced the notation SA to denote spiral galaxies without bars, complementing Hubble's use of SB for barred spirals.

He also allowed for an intermediate class, denoted SAB, containing weakly barred spirals. Lenticular galaxies are also classified as unbarred (SA0) or barred (SB0), with the notation S0 reserved for those galaxies for which it is impossible to tell if a bar is present or not (usually because they are edge-on to the line-of-sight).

Rings. Galaxies are divided into those possessing ring-like structures (denoted '(r)') and those without rings (denoted '(s)'). So-called 'transition' galaxies are given the symbol (rs).

Spiral arms. As in Hubble's original scheme, spiral galaxies are assigned to a class based primarily on the tightness of their spiral arms. The de Vaucouleurs scheme extends the arms of Hubble's tuning fork to include several additional spiral classes:

Sd (SBd) - diffuse, broken arms made up of individual stellar clusters and nebulae; very faint central bulge
Sm (SBm) - irregular in appearance; no bulge component
Im - highly irregular galaxy

Most galaxies in these three classes were classified as Irr I in Hubble's original scheme. In addition, the Sd class contains some galaxies from Hubble's Sc class. Galaxies in the classes Sm and Im are termed the "Magellanic" spirals and irregulars, respectively, after the Magellanic Clouds. The Large Magellanic Cloud is of type SBm, while the Small Magellanic Cloud is an irregular (Im). The different elements of the classification scheme are combined — in the order in which they are listed — to give the complete classification of a galaxy. For example, a weakly barred spiral galaxy with loosely wound arms and a ring is denoted SAB(r)c.

Visually, the de Vaucouleurs system can be represented as a three-dimensional version of Hubble's tuning fork, with stage (spiralness) on the x-axis, family (barredness) on the y-axis, and variety (ringedness) on the z-axis. [R80]

Observation:

This excerpt is not the complete topic but covers the important details. This is enough to understand most of the galaxies listed in my galaxy data set.

Note: AGN is sometimes found in descriptions of galaxies or quasars. AGN is short for Active Galactic Nucleus.

AGN refers to an electromagnetic entity in the nucleus generating intense radiation spanning a broad range of wavelengths from X-ray to radio. An AGN is a source of synchrotron radiation, a term explained in section Light.

Internal mechanisms in galaxies were covered in my earlier books and are not completely repeated here. This book is about correctly measuring the velocity of galaxies from on or near the Earth, not about their AGN.

7.2 Seyfert Galaxy

A Seyfert galaxy is a special type of a spiral galaxy.

Seyfert galaxies are one of the two largest groups of active galaxies, along with quasars. They have quasar-like nuclei (very luminous, distant, and bright sources of electromagnetic radiation) with very high surface brightnesses whose spectra reveal strong, high-ionisation emission lines, but unlike quasars, their host galaxies are clearly detectable.

Seyfert galaxies account for about 10% of all galaxies and are some of the most intensely studied objects in astronomy, as they are thought to be powered by the same phenomena that occur in quasars, although they are closer and less luminous than quasars. [R81]

Observation:

This description reveals the lack of understanding the mechanisms driving the behaviors of a spiral galaxy. A spiral galaxy model defined by Donald Scott was described in an earlier book. A very brief explanation summary here is the spiral galaxy has an axial electrical current from its host cluster. This current generates the galactic magnetic field. The magnetic field generates the Lorentz force driving the disk rotation because stars have a positive charge.

At the galactic core, the current both bends and splits to provide a current out each spiral arm to deliver a current to the stars there.

When an electric current's path changes due to a magnetic field, the result is synchrotron radiation. The velocity of the current drives the peak frequency in the synchrotron radiation distribution of energy. A very fast current achieves X-ray wavelength energy. Nearly every spiral galaxy has its point source of X-rays in its core from this mechanism. The electric current along the galaxy's axis bends to go out the spiral arms. This axial current also generates the galactic magnetic field driving the disk rotation.

There is absolutely no dark matter. Any place where this invisible, undetectable entity is proposed, there is a magnetic field being ignored.

7.3 Galaxy examples.

The following are spectrum samples from several Messier objects. These are all from NED, or the NASA Extragalactic Database. [R24]

That site offers a simple display with s sequence of:

1) The object's name is entered into an entry field,

2) Click on Go,
3) Wait for the object to be found. Acceptable names can include an NGC number, or another name. For example, either M31 or NGC 224 gets the Andromeda galaxy.

Some objects have more pages of data than others.

The Spectra tab / selection shows the number of spectra recorded for the object. At the top right is the spectrum band, like Optical or Mid-IR, or UV, or even an emission line.
At the left of the NED page are images. Clicking on an image zooms in.

7.4 M31

M31 is a spiral galaxy in the Local Group.

Here is its spectrogram showing the optical wavelength band:

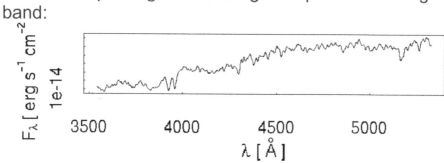

There are 2 dips below 4000 Angstroms. Those are the 2 absorption lines from calcium ions in the line of sight to M31.

The blue shift in those absorption lines is the justification of the M31 relative velocity of 401 km/s toward Earth.

Atoms in the line of sight cannot be used to measure a large galaxy. This velocity is a mistake.

Here is its spectrogram in the ultraviolet wavelength band:

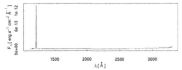

There is a strong emission line around 1215 Angstroms. That wavelength will be described below.

7.5 M33

M33 is a spiral galaxy in the Local Group.

Here is its spectrogram in the optical wavelength band:

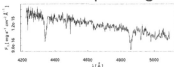

The spectrogram in NED for M33 has a slightly different span of wavelengths than for M31.

Both galaxies show the signature of synchrotron radiation with the range of wavelengths from ultraviolet to infrared having a similar intensity. Each dip is from atoms in the line of sight absorbing their characteristic wavelengths.

M33 has several absorption lines from atoms in the line of sight. They are the justification of the M33 relative velocity of 179 km/s toward Earth. Atoms in the line of sight cannot be used to measure a galaxy's velocity. This value is a mistake.

Here is the M33 spectrogram in the ultraviolet wavelength band:

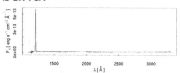

Just like with M31, there is a strong emission line near 1216 Angstroms.

7.6 Lyman Alpha Emitter Galaxy

A Lyman-alpha emitter (LAE) is a type of distant galaxy that emits Lyman-alpha radiation from neutral hydrogen. Most known LAEs are extremely distant, and because of the finite travel time of light they provide glimpses into the history of the universe. They are thought to be the progenitors of most modern Milky Way type galaxies.

The baryonic acoustic oscillation signal should be evident in the power spectrum of Lyman-alpha emitters at high redshift. Baryonic acoustic oscillations are imprints of sound waves on scales where radiation pressure stabilized the density perturbations against gravitational collapse in the early universe. The three-dimensional distribution of the characteristically homogeneous Lyman-alpha galaxy population will allow a robust probe of cosmology.

They are a good tool because the Lyman-alpha bias, the propensity for galaxies to form in the highest overdensity of the underlying dark matter distribution, can be modeled and accounted for. Lyman-alpha emitters are over dense in clusters. [R86]

Observation:

This description reveals much confusion. First, the Lyman-alpha emission line occurs a proton captures an electron, and the electron drops to the hydrogen ground state.

References to "baryonic acoustic oscillation" are meaningless. Attempts to model "dark matter distribution" are meaningless. There is no dark matter. That mistake is covered in the TFR part of section NED Distances.

This Lyman-alpha emission occurs from an event in the line of sight to a galaxy. That event is a proton capturing an electron. This event cannot be related to the galaxy. Trying to link this event to the age of a galaxy is unjustified and ridiculous. Plasmoids, like the one in M87, emit jets of plasma, often superluminal. If a particular galaxy happens to be in the path of these superluminal jets, then it could be a LAE.

8 Galaxies with Cepheids

The use of Cepheid variable stars was mentioned in previous sections. They are covered in more detail here.

Cepheids are crucial to cosmology as the most reliable mechanism for getting a galaxy's distance.

Light has a well-known behavior of dimming by distance.

If a known light source is observed in a distant galaxy, then its distance can be calculated using the measured reduction in the light intensity.

Several types of variable stars have been identified, where the combination of a maximum magnitude, a minimum magnitude, and the time between the 2 peaks follow a consistent pattern.
A Cepheid variable is a candidate for that application.

Cepheids have served another, crucial role in cosmology.

When its galaxy has its distance calculated, this exercise gets the red shift velocity associated with a distance, which are the units of Hubble's constant.

The Cepheid enables the measurement of the claimed relationship between a redshift velocity and the object's distance. The Cepheid provides a distance from Earth. The velocity is a separate measurement.

Unfortunately for cosmology, only 17 galaxies beyond our Local Group have been found containing Cepheids. Despite this relatively low number among the 1000's of galaxies, their distribution and their data obtained by current methods enabled many important conclusions about these:

a) The method of measuring a redshift velocity,

b) The method of measuring a distance to a galaxy having Cepheid,

c) The publication of those values,

d) The assumed consistency of the universe expansion as presented by Hubble's constant.

By its very name, cosmologists expect Hubble's constant to describe the uniform expansion of the universe where a redshift velocity from any object in the universe is directly related to a distance using a single constant value. That directly implies an unjustified assumption of a uniform expansion of the universe. Unfortunately for that assumption, all galaxies have their velocity measured incorrectly. They are measured like a star, but their spectra are too different making this method a mistake.

Here is my list of the 17 galaxies with Cepheids beyond our Local Group:

Name	other name	constell.	quad	list
NGC 2403	Caldwell 7	Camelop.	NQ2	1
NGC 3351	M95	Leo	NQ2	2
NGC 3368	M96	Leo	NQ2	3
NGC 3198	Herschel 146	Ursa Major	NQ2	4
NGC 4321	M100	Como Berenices	NQ3	5
NGC 4548	M91	Como Berenices	NQ3	6
NGC 4725		Como Berenices	NQ3	7
NGC 7331		Pegasus	NQ4	8
NGC 300	Caldwell 70	Sculptor	SQ1	9
NGC 1365		Fornax	SQ1	10
NGC 3621		Hydra	SQ2	11
NGC 5236	M83	Hydra	SQ2	12
NGC 4038	Antennae	Corvus	SQ3	13
NGC 5128	Centaurus A	Centaurus	SQ3	14
NGC 5253		Centaurus	SQ3	15
NGC 4535		Virgo	SQ3	16
NGC 4536		Virgo	SQ3	17

The 17 are not in a uniform distribution around the sky, beyond our Local Group and our Milky Way.

Those too close, or are in the Local Group, are excluded. Edwin Hubble declared: the Local Group is an island separate from the Hubble Flow, so I expect Hubble's law and constant do not apply within the Local Group. The galaxies having Cepheids are found in 6 of the 8 sky quadrants.
Some are somewhat close to another in the same constellation. Several are in the Virgo galaxy cluster, which spans several quadrants.

A description of each galaxy's measurements will follow.

Many spectra are presented here with the final public values derived from them, including important statements in NED which must be noted when affecting how the values should be treated.

8.1 NGC 2403

NGC 2403 is also known as Caldwell 7, and is in the constellation Camelopardalis, in sky quadrant NQ2.

From NED Redshifts (37):

Preferred Redshift: Z = 0.00044, H0 = 67.8 km/sec/Mpc, Ω matter = 0.308, Ω vacuum = 0.692

V (Heliocentric) is 133 km/sec

Hubble Flow Distance and Distance Modulus (where H0 = 67.8 km/sec/Mpc ± km/sec/Mpc)

D (Local Group) = 3.99 Mpc

Cosmology-Corrected Quantities [H0 = 67.8 km/sec/Mpc, Ω matter = 0.308, Ω vacuum = 0.692]

[Redshift 0.000608 as corrected to the Reference Frame defined by the 3K CMB]

Observations:

1)
Calculating V from Z and c is 132 km/s
The V result difference of 1 km/s is trivial.

2)
Calculating D from NED V and H0 is 1.932153 Mpc
The D result is about half from NED

3)
 From Wikipedia:
V = 131 km/s
D = 2.96 Mpc

Wikipedia V matches NED V
But D values differ

4) Any reference to the CMB is alarming because there is
no CMB, only noise from Earth's oceans which was
mistaken for the hypothetical CMB.

From NED Distances (65):

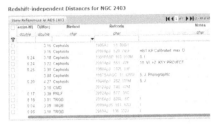

There are 7 results for Method Cepheids

Their average = 3.1557143

There are 7 results from other methods (not all fit in the screen capture).

The average of the 14 = 3.1635714

The D provided by NED is not just from this set.

Wikipedia D does not match NED.

From NED Spectra (37):

Here are the relevant ones:

Image 1, UV band, from Nucleus region.

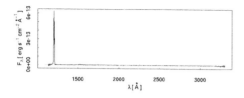

Image 2, H I, from integrated region.

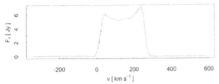

Image 2, Optical band, from Nucleus region.

Observations:

Image 1)

Lyman-alpha emission line was detected in UV band. It appears close to 1216 A, so the proton was not moving fast at the moment of electron capture.

This event detection has nothing to do with a galaxy's velocity or distance.

Image 2)

There is no spectrum provided for this plot of velocities. The only possible origin of this plot is a number of emission lines around 21 cm. Each line had its wavelength measured from 21 cm. The difference was compared to 21 cm where diff / 21 cm = z. Next, each z was multiplied by c, resulting in a series of velocity and wavelength intensity as shown.

It is impossible for this set of atoms in the line of sight, having differences in their 21 cm emission line to indicate the galaxy's proper velocity.

The peak to the left is probably around 131, the stated velocity. The peak to the right is probably around 220.

Neither of these peaks can be the galaxy's velocity in any direction. Using them is a mistake.

It is impossible to measure any 3-dimensional proper velocity when using only the line of sight.

NGC 2403 has an unjustified non-zero velocity.

This exercise requires measuring motion in all directions including transverse. It is a mistake of negligence when measuring only in the line of sight. The velocity measurement requires many positions recorded over a span of time. This is how we measure the motion of comets and asteroids. Galaxies are more distant and require more time because the angular distance covered in time decreases as the distance increases, for the same velocity.

NGC 2403 has a wrong velocity when derived from atoms.

It is impossible to calculate the V/D ratio, or Hubble's constant, for this galaxy.

8.2 NGC 3351

NGC 3351 is also known as M95, and is in the constellation Leo, in sky quadrant NQ2.

From NED Redshifts (35):

Preferred Redshift: Z = 0.00260, H0 = 67.8 km/sec/Mpc, Ωmatter = 0.308, Ω vacuum = 0.692

V (Heliocentric) is 778 ± 4 km/s km/sec

Hubble Flow Distance and Distance Modulus (where H0 = 67.8 km/sec/Mpc ± km/sec/Mpc)

D (Local Group) 9.20 ± 0.66 Mpc

Cosmology-Corrected Quantities [H0 = 67.8 km/sec/Mpc, Ω matter = 0.308, Ω vacuum = 0.692]

[Redshift 0.003758 as corrected to the Reference Frame defined by the 3K CMB]

Observations:

1)
Calculating V from Z and c is 780 km/s
The V result difference of 2 km/s is trivial.

2)
Calculating D from NED V and H0 is 11.50442 Mpc
The D result is about 10% higher than NED

3)
From Wikipedia:
V = 778 km/s
D = 10 Mpc

Wikipedia V matches NED V
But D values differ

From NED Distances (62):

There are 20 results for Method Cepheids (not all fit in the screen capture).

Their average = 9.9255

There are over 20 results from other methods (could not fit in the screen capture).

The D provided by NED is not just from this set.

Wikipedia D does not match NED.

From NED Spectra (30):

The relevant images are provided:

Image 1, UV band, from Nucleus region.

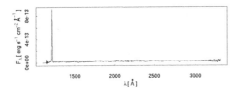

Image 2, H I, from integrated region.

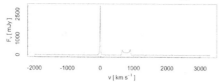

Image 3, Optical band, from Nucleus region.

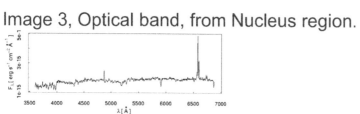

Image 4, Optical band, from Integrated-Drift Scan region.

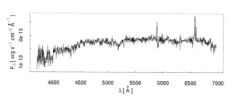

Observations:

Image 1)

Lyman-alpha emission line was detected in UV band. It appears close to 1216 A so the proton was not moving fast at the moment of electron capture.

This event detection has nothing to do with a galaxy's velocity or distance.

Image 2)

There is no spectrum provided for this plot of velocities. The only possible origin of this plot is some number of emission lines around 21 cm. There was a strong line at exactly 21 cm, so its z=0, implying 0 velocity. Each other line had its wavelength measured from 21 cm. The difference was compared to 21 cm where diff / 21 cm = z. Next, each z was multiplied by c, resulting in a series of velocities with wavelength intensity as shown.

It is impossible for this set of atoms in the line of sight, having a mix of differences in their 21 cm emission line to indicate the galaxy's proper velocity. The strong non-shifted line was ignored so the weaker, shifted lines could provide a non-zero velocity, when a measurement of zero velocity could be justified for this galaxy based on the H I lines.

The claimed velocity of 778 is apparently from the much weaker emission lines which had a shift.

None of these peaks can be the galaxy's velocity in any direction. Using them is a mistake.

It is impossible to measure any 3-dimensional proper velocity when using only the line of sight.

Images 3 and 4)

6563 A is the Balmer-alpha emission line, and it seems to be captured by both samples. The line suggests a slow proton captured a slow electron, emitting less energy than the Lyman-alpha line, when the atom dropped to ground state, resulting in no significant shift of the line.

NGC 3351 has an unjustified non-zero velocity. The correct value is the statement: there has been no attempt to measure this galaxy's proper 3-D velocity.

This exercise requires measuring motion in all directions including transverse. It is a mistake of negligence when measuring only in the line of sight. The velocity measurement requires many positions recorded over a span of time. This is how we measure the motion of comets and asteroids. Galaxies are more distant and require more time because the angular distance covered in time decreases as the distance increases, for the same velocity.

NGC 3351 should have a published statement which directly states there is a range of possible distances from multiple Cepheids. The value must state the uncertainty which is demonstrated by the many different possible values coming from different attempts. A distance being derived from 20 or more values should not omit the uncertainty.

NGC 3351 has a wrong velocity.

It is impossible to calculate the V/D ratio, or Hubble's constant, for this galaxy.

8.3 NGC 3368

NGC 3368 is also known as M96, and is in the constellation Leo, in sky quadrant NQ2.

From NED Redshifts (28):

Preferred Redshift: Z = 0.00299, H0 = 67.8 km/sec/Mpc, Ω matter = 0.308, Ω vacuum = 0.692

V (Heliocentric) is 897 ± 4 km/s

Hubble Flow Distance and Distance Modulus (where H0 = 67.8 km/sec/Mpc ± km/sec/Mpc)

D (Local Group) = 10.98 ± 0.78 Mpc

Cosmology-Corrected Quantities [H0 = 67.8 km/sec/Mpc, Ω matter = 0.308, Ω vacuum = 0.692]

[Redshift 0.004156 as corrected to the Reference Frame defined by the 3K CMB]

Observations:

1)
Calculating V from Z and c is 897 km/s
The V result matches NED.

2)
Calculating D from NED V and H0 is 13.23009 Mpc
The D result is about 20% higher than NED

3)
 From Wikipedia:
V = 897 km/s
D = 9.6 Mpc

Wikipedia V matches NED V
But D values differ

From NED Distances (71):

Redshift-independent Distances for MESSIER 096

There are 21 results for Method Cepheids (not all fit in the screen capture)

Their average = 11.022857

There are more than 20 results from other methods (not all fit in the screen capture).

The distance provided by NED is not just from this set.

Wikipedia D does not match NED.

From NED Spectra (13):

Here are the relevant images:

Image 1, H I, from integrated region.

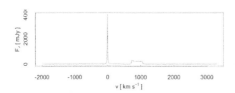

Image 2, Optical band, from Integrated-Drift Scan region.

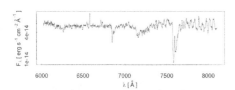

Image 3, Optical band, from Nucleus region.

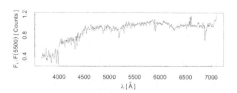

Image 4, H I, from integrated region.

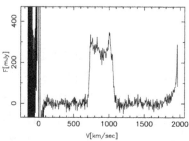

There are more H I spectra in NED than presented here.

Observations:

Image 1)

There is no spectrum provided for this plot of velocities. The only possible origin of this plot is several emission lines around 21 cm. Each line had its wavelength measured from 21 cm. The difference was compared to 21 cm where diff / 21 cm = z. Next, each z was multiplied by c, resulting in a series of velocity with wavelength intensity as shown.

The image is noteworthy because the strong velocity at zero means there is a strong non-shifted 21 cm line. As that must be the strongest line in the hidden spectrum, a zero velocity for this galaxy could be justified. Instead, the claimed velocity apparently was found in the weaker lines which were red shifted.

It is impossible for this set of atoms in the line of sight, having differences in their 21 cm emission line to indicate the galaxy's proper velocity.

None of these peaks can be the galaxy's velocity in any direction. Using them is a mistake.

It is impossible to measure any 3-dimensional proper velocity when using only the line of sight.

NGC 3368 has an unjustified non-zero velocity.

This exercise requires measuring motion in all directions including transverse. It is a mistake of negligence when measuring only in the line of sight. The velocity measurement requires many positions recorded over a span of time. This is how we measure the motion of comets and asteroids. Galaxies are more distant and require more time because the angular distance covered in time decreases as the distance increases, for the same velocity.

NGC 3368 should have a published statement which directly states there is a range of possible distances. The value must state the uncertainty which is demonstrated by the many different possible distances coming from different attempts. A distance being derived from 21 or more values should not omit the uncertainty.

NGC 3368 has a wrong velocity when derived from atoms.

It is impossible to calculate the V/D ratio, or Hubble's constant, for this galaxy.

8.4 NGC 3198

NGC 3198 is also known as Herschel 146, and is in the constellation Ursa Major, in sky quadrant NQ2.

From NED Redshifts (27):

Preferred Redshift: Z = 0.00220, H0 = 67.8 km/sec/Mpc, Ωmatter = 0.308, Ω vacuum = 0.692

V (Heliocentric) is 660 km/sec

Hubble Flow Distance and Distance Modulus (where H0 = 67.8 km/sec/Mpc ± km/sec/Mpc)

D (Local Group) = 10.02 ± 0.70 Mpc

Cosmology-Corrected Quantities [H0 = 67.8 km/sec/Mpc, Ωmatter = 0.308, Ω vacuum = 0.692]

[Redshift 0.002933 as corrected to the Reference Frame defined by the 3K CMB]

Observations:

1)
Calculating V from Z and c is 660 km/s
The V result matches NED
2)
Calculating D from NED V and H0 is 9.734513 Mpc
The D result is about 3% below D from NED

3)

 From Wikipedia:
Z = 0.00227 or V = 681 km/s
D = 14.4172 Mpc

Wikipedia V and D differ from NED

From NED Distances (52):

There are 21 distance results for Method Cepheids

Their average = 14.67619 Mpc

There are over 10 results from other methods (not all fit in the screen capture).

The D provided by NED is not from just this set.

From NED Spectra (25):

Here are the relevant images:

Image 1, Optical band, from Nucleus region.

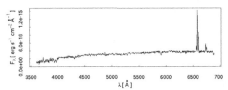

Image 2, Optical band, from integrated region.

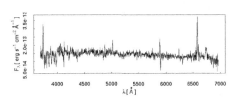

Image 3, Optical band, from Nucleus region.

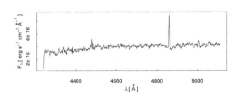

Image 4, H I, from integrated region.

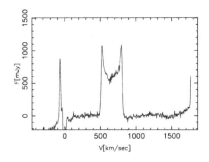

Image 5, H I, from integrated region.

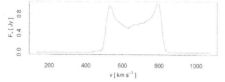

Image 6, H I, from integrated region.

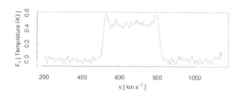

Image 7, O I line, from nucleus region.

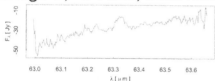

There are also spectrum captures of O III line, and C II line.
All metallic lines must be ignored, as none can be related to the galaxy's real velocity.

Observations:

Images 1-3)

6563 A is the Balmer-alpha emission line, and seems to be captured by these samples. The line suggests a slow proton captured a slow electron, emitting less energy than the Lyman-alpha line, when the atom dropped to its ground state, resulting in no shift of the line.

This line's detection has nothing to do with a galaxy's velocity or distance.

Images 4-6)

There is no spectrum provided for each plot of velocities. The only possible origin of this plot is several emission lines around 21 cm. Each line had its wavelength measured from 21 cm. The difference was compared to 21 cm where diff / 21 cm = z. Next, each z was multiplied by c, resulting in a series of a velocity with a wavelength intensity as shown.

Neither of these H I peaks can be the galaxy's velocity in any direction. Using them is a mistake.

It is impossible for this set of atoms in the line of sight, having differences in their 21 cm emission line to indicate the galaxy's proper velocity.

The peak in image 4 was probably used for the galaxy velocity, not from images 5 and 6.

NED never explicitly identifies the spectrum used for the velocity value.

Image 7 reveals checking for metallic lines, including oxygen and carbon.

No metallic line, regardless of absorption or emission, can indicate the galaxy's velocity in any direction. Using them is a mistake.

It is impossible to measure any 3-dimensional proper velocity when using only the line of sight.

NGC 3198 has an unjustified non-zero velocity.

This exercise requires measuring motion in all directions including transverse. It is a mistake of negligence when measuring only in the line of sight. The velocity measurement requires many positions recorded over a span of time. This is how we measure the motion of comets and asteroids. Galaxies are more distant and require more time because the angular distance covered in time decreases as the distance increases, for the same velocity.

NGC 3198 should have a published statement which directly states there is a range of possible distances from multiple Cepheids. The value must state the uncertainty which is demonstrated by the many different possible values coming from different attempts. A distance being derived from 7 or more values should not omit the uncertainty.

NGC 3198 has a wrong velocity when derived from atoms.

It is impossible to calculate the V/D ratio, or Hubble's constant, for this galaxy, when both numerator and denominator are lists of values.

8.5 NGC 4321

NGC 4321 is also known as M100, and is in the constellation Como Berenices, in sky quadrant NQ3.

From NED Redshifts (40):

Preferred Redshift: Z = 0.00524, H0 = 67.8 km/sec/Mpc, Ωmatter = 0.308, Ω vacuum = 0.692
V (Heliocentric) is 1571 ± 1 km/s

Hubble Flow Distance and Distance Modulus (where H0 = 67.8 km/sec/Mpc ± km/sec/Mpc)

D (Local Group) = 21.80 ± 1.53 Mpc

Cosmology-Corrected Quantities [H0 = 67.8 km/sec/Mpc, Ωmatter = 0.308, Ω vacuum = 0.692]
[Redshift 0.006325 as corrected to the Reference Frame defined by the 3K CMB]

Observations:

1)
Calculating V from Z and c is 1572 km/s
The V result difference of 1 km/s is trivial.

2)
Calculating D from NED V and H0 is 23.18584 Mpc
The D result is about 6% higher than NED

3)
 From Wikipedia:
V = 1571 km/s
D =16.8712 Mpc

Wikipedia V matches NED V
But D values differ

From NED Distances (70):

Redshift-independent Distances for MESSIER 100

There are 25 results for Method Cepheids (not all fit in the screen capture)

Their average = 16.016

There are more results from other methods (not all fit in the screen capture).
The numbers provided by NED cannot be duplicated.

Wikipedia D does not match NED.

From NED Spectra (32):

Here are the relevant images:

Image 1, UV band, from Nucleus region.

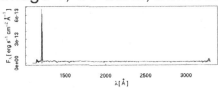

Image 2, H I, from integrated region.

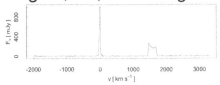

Image 3, Optical band, from Nucleus region.

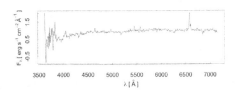

Image 4, Optical band, from Nucleus region.

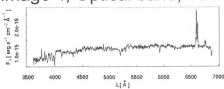

Image 5, H I, from integrated region.

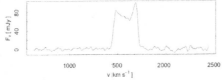

region.

Image 6, H I, from integrated region.

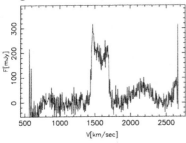

Observations:

Image 1)

Lyman-alpha emission line was detected in UV band. It appears close to 1216 A so it was not moving fast at the moment of electron capture.

This event detection has nothing to do with a galaxy's velocity or distance.

Images 2, 5, 6)

There is no spectrum provided for this plot of velocities. The only possible origin of this plot is a number of emission lines around 21 cm. Each line had its wavelength measured from 21 cm. The difference was compared to 21 cm where diff / 21 cm = z. Next, each z was multiplied by c, resulting in a series of velocity with wavelength intensity as shown.

It is impossible for this set of atoms in the line of sight, having differences in their 21 cm emission line to indicate the galaxy's proper velocity.

The strongest peak was at $z = 0$. A zero velocity is justified for this galaxy. However weaker lines were used to claim a non-zero velocity.

None of these peaks can be the galaxy's velocity in any direction. Using them is a mistake.

It is impossible to measure any 3-dimensional proper velocity when using only the line of sight.

NGC 4321 has an unjustified non-zero velocity.

This exercise requires measuring motion in all directions including transverse. It is a mistake of negligence when measuring only in the line of sight. The velocity measurement requires many positions recorded over a span of time. This is how we measure the motion of comets and asteroids. Galaxies are more distant and require more time because the angular distance covered in time decreases as the distance increases, for the same velocity.

NGC 4321 should have a published statement which directly states there is a range of possible distances. The value must state the uncertainty which is demonstrated by the many different possible values coming from different attempts. A distance being derived from 7 or more values should not omit the uncertainty.

NGC 4321 has a wrong velocity when derived from atoms.

It is impossible to calculate the V/D ratio, or Hubble's constant, for this galaxy.

8.6 NGC 4548

NGC 4548 is also known as M91, and is in the constellation Leo, in sky quadrant NQ2.

From NED Redshifts (22):

Preferred Redshift: Z = 0.00162, H0 = 67.8 km/sec/Mpc, Ω matter = 0.308, Ω vacuum = 0.692

V (Heliocentric) is 486 ± 4 km/s

Hubble Flow Distance and Distance Modulus (where H0 = 67.8 km/sec/Mpc ± km/sec/Mpc)

D (Local Group) = 5.82 ± 0.42 Mpc

Cosmology-Corrected Quantities [H0 = 67.8 km/sec/Mpc, Ω matter = 0.308, Ω vacuum = 0.692]

[Redshift 0.002695 as corrected to the Reference Frame defined by the 3K CMB]

Observations:

1)
Calculating V from Z and c is 486 km/s
The V result matches NED

2)
Calculating D from NED V and H0 = 7.168142 Mpc
The D result is 23% higher than NED

3)
From Wikipedia:
V = 486 km/s
D = 19 Mpc

Wikipedia V matches NED V
But D values differ

From NED Distances (42):

There are 21 results for Method Cepheids

Their average = 15.584211

There are more results from other methods (not all fit in the screen capture).

The D provided by NED is not just from this set.

Wikipedia D does not match NED.

From NED Spectra (8):

Here are the relevant ones:

Image 1, Optical band, from Nucleus region.

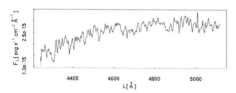

Image 2, H I, from Nucleus region.

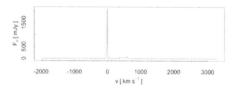

Image 3, H I, from integrated region.

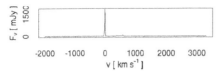

Image 4, Optical band, from integrated region.

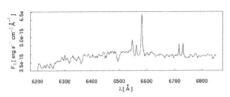

Observations:

Image 1)

There are some absorption and emission lines but are inconsistent, making a selection unjustified.

Images 2, 3)

There is no spectrum provided for the plots of velocities. The only possible origin of this plot is some number of emission lines around 21 cm. Each line had its wavelength measured from 21 cm. The difference was compared to 21 cm where diff / 21 cm = z. Next, each z was multiplied by c, resulting in a series of velocity with wavelength intensity as shown.

It is impossible for this set of atoms in the line of sight, having differences in their 21 cm emission line to indicate the galaxy's proper velocity.

The tiny peak is probably around 486, the stated velocity. Its low intensity justifies its validity for consideration.

Neither of these peaks can be the galaxy's velocity in any direction. Using them is a mistake.

Image 4)

6563 A is the Balmer-alpha emission line, and seems to be slightly blue shifted. The line suggests a slow proton captured a slow electron, emitting less energy than the Lyman-alpha line, when the atom dropped to ground state, and its motion toward the observer resulted in a blue shift of the line. Blue shifts are rare and this possible measurement of one was not used, for this galaxy. Regardless of its shift, the line indicates nothing of the galaxy.

It is impossible to measure any 3-dimensional proper velocity when using only the line of sight.

NGC 4548 has an unjustified non-zero velocity.

This exercise requires measuring motion in all directions including transverse. It is a mistake of negligence when measuring only in the line of sight.

The velocity measurement requires many positions recorded over a span of time. This is how we measure the motion of comets and asteroids. Galaxies are more distant and require more time because the angular distance covered in time decreases as the distance increases, for the same velocity.

NGC 4548 should have a published statement which directly states there is a range of possible distances. The value must state the uncertainty which is demonstrated by the many different possible values coming from different attempts. A distance being derived from 21 or more values should not omit the uncertainty.

NGC 4548 has a wrong velocity when derived from atoms.

It is impossible to calculate the V/D ratio, or Hubble's constant, for this galaxy.

8.7 NGC 4725

NGC 4725 is in the constellation Leo, in sky quadrant NQ2.

From NED Redshifts (28):

Preferred Redshift: $Z = 0.00402$, H0 = 67.8 km/sec/Mpc, Ω matter = 0.308, Ω vacuum = 0.692

V (Heliocentric) is 1206 ± 3 km/s

Hubble Flow Distance and Distance Modulus (where H0 = 67.8 km/sec/Mpc ± km/sec/Mpc)

D (Local Group) = 17.34 ± 1.21 Mpc

Cosmology-Corrected Quantities [H0 = 67.8 km/sec/Mpc, Ω matter = 0.308, Ω vacuum = 0.692]

[Redshift 0.004966 as corrected to the Reference Frame defined by the 3K CMB]

Observations:

1)
Calculating V from uncorrected Z and c is 1206 km/s
The V result is the same as NED.

2)
Calculating D from NED V and H0 17.78761 Mpc
The D result is about 2% higher than NED

3)

From Wikipedia:
V = 1206 km/s
D = 12.3 Mpc

Wikipedia V matches NED V
But D values differ BY about 40%

From NED Distances (48):

There are 17 results for Method Cepheids (not all fit in the screen capture).

Their average = 13.141176

There are more than 10 results from other methods (not all fit in the screen capture).

The D provided by NED is not just from this set.

Wikipedia D does not match NED.

From NED Spectra (29):

Here are the relevant ones:

Image 1, H I, from integrated region.

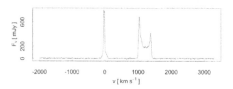

Image 2, Optical band, from Nucleus region.

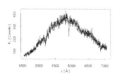

Image 3, O I line, from Nucleus region.

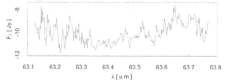

Image 4, H I, from integrated region.

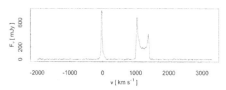

Observations:

Images 1 and 4)

There is no spectrum provided for each plot of velocities. The only possible origin of this plot is several emission lines around 21 cm. Each line had its wavelength measured from 21 cm. The difference was compared to 21 cm where diff / 21 cm = z. Next, each z was multiplied by c, resulting in a series of velocity with wavelength intensity as shown.

It is impossible for this set of atoms in the line of sight, having differences in their 21 cm emission line to indicate the galaxy's proper velocity.

The peak is not at the value of 1206. NED never identifies the spectrum providing the velocity value.

None of these peaks can be the galaxy's velocity in any direction. Using them is a mistake.

It is impossible to measure any 3-dimensional proper velocity when using only the line of sight.

NGC 4725 has an unjustified non-zero velocity.

This exercise requires measuring motion in all directions including transverse. It is a mistake of negligence when measuring only in the line of sight. The velocity measurement requires many positions recorded over a span of time. This is how we measure the motion of comets and asteroids. Galaxies are more distant and require more time because the angular distance covered in time decreases as the distance increases, for the same velocity.

NGC 4725 should have a published statement which directly states there is a range of possible distances. The value must state the uncertainty which is demonstrated by the many different possible values coming from different attempts. A distance being derived from 7 or more values should not omit the uncertainty.

NGC 4725 has a wrong velocity when derived from atoms.

It is impossible to calculate the V/D ratio, or Hubble's constant, for this galaxy.

8.8 NGC 7331

NGC 7331 is in the constellation Leo, in sky quadrant NQ2
Pegasus NQ4.

From NED Redshifts (35):

Preferred Redshift: $Z = 0.00272$, $H0 = 67.8$ km/sec/Mpc, Ω matter $= 0.308$, Ω vacuum $= 0.692$

V (Heliocentric) is 816 ± 1 km/s

Hubble Flow Distance and Distance Modulus (where $H0 = 67.8$ km/sec/Mpc $\pm$ km/sec/Mpc)

D (Local Group) $= 16.50 \pm 1.19$ Mpc

Cosmology-Corrected Quantities [$H0 = 67.8$ km/sec/Mpc, Ω matter $= 0.308$, Ω vacuum $= 0.692$]

[Redshift 0.001635 as corrected to the Reference Frame defined by the 3K CMB]

Observations:

1)
Calculating V from uncorrected Z and c is 816 km/s
The V result matches NED.

2)
Calculating D from NED V and H0 is 12.0354 Mpc
The D result is about 73% that from NED.

3)
 From Wikipedia:
V = 816 km/s
D = 12.2 Mpc

Wikipedia V matches NED V
But D values differ

From NED Distances (54):

There are 17 results for Method Cepheids

Their average = 14.90625
There are also results from other methods (not all fit in the
screen capture).

The D provided by NED is not just from this set.

Wikipedia does not match NED.

From NED Spectra:

The tab has (17)

The relevant ones:

Image 1, Optical band, from Nucleus region.

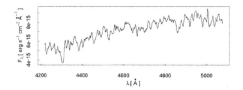

Image 2, Optical band, from Nucleus region.

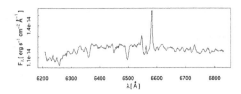

Image 3, H I. from Integrated region.

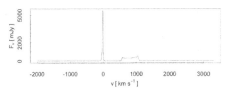

Image 4, H I. from Integrated region.

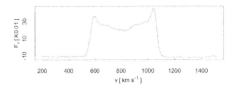

Image 5, H I. from Integrated region.

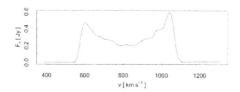

Image 6, H I. from Integrated region.

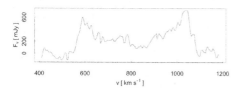

Image 7, H I. from Integrated region.

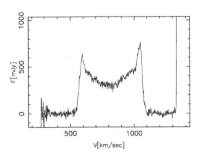

Observations:

Image 1)

There are no prominent emission lines to select one for a red shift.

Image 2)

6563 A is the Balmer-alpha emission line, and seems to be redshifted. The line suggests a slow proton captured a slow electron, emitting less energy than the Lyman-alpha line, when the atom dropped to ground state, and its motion away from the observer resulted in a red shift of the line.
Perhaps the astronomer made the correct conclusion when ignoring this line.

(Images 3-7)

There is no spectrum provided for this plot of velocities. The only possible origin of this plot is some number of emission lines around 21 cm. Each line had its wavelength measured from 21 cm. The difference was compared to 21 cm where diff / 21 cm = z. Next, each z was multiplied by c, resulting in a series of velocity with wavelength intensity as shown.

It is impossible for this set of atoms in the line of sight, having differences in their 21 cm emission line to indicate the galaxy's proper velocity.

Image 3 might have a peak around 816, the stated velocity.

NED never explicitly identifies the spectrum used for the velocity value.

None of these peaks can be the galaxy's velocity in any direction. Using them is a mistake.

It is impossible to measure any 3-dimensional proper velocity when using only the line of sight.

NGC 7331 has an unjustified non-zero velocity. The correct value is the statement: there has been no attempt to measure this galaxy's proper velocity.

This exercise requires measuring motion in all directions including transverse. It is a mistake of negligence when measuring only in the line of sight. The velocity measurement requires many positions recorded over a span of time. This is how we measure the motion of comets and asteroids. Galaxies are more distant and require more time because the angular distance covered in time decreases as the distance increases, for the same velocity.

NGC 7331 should have a published statement which directly states there is a range of possible distances. The value must state the uncertainty which is demonstrated by the many different possible values coming from different attempts. A distance being derived from 17 or more values should not omit the uncertainty.

If any values are altered to account for the non-existent CMB, then each change is invalid and anything affected by this mistake must be fixed. NED is not explicit with what changed for the CMB.

NGC 7331 has a wrong velocity.

It is impossible to calculate the V/D ratio, or Hubble's constant, for this galaxy, when both numerator and denominator are lists of values.

8.9 NGC 300

NGC 300 is also known as Caldwell 70, and is in the constellation Sculptor, in sky quadrant SQ1.

From NED Redshifts (20):

Preferred Redshift: Z = 0.00048, H0 = 67.8 km/sec/Mpc, Ω matter = 0.308, Ω vacuum = 0.692

V (Heliocentric) is 144 ± 1 km/s

Hubble Flow Distance and Distance Modulus (where H0 = 67.8 km/sec/Mpc ± km/sec/Mpc)

D (Local Group) = 1.68 ± 0.12 Mpc

Cosmology-Corrected Quantities [H0 = 67.8 km/sec/Mpc, Ω matter = 0.308, Ω vacuum = 0.692]

[Redshift -0.000304 as corrected to the Reference Frame defined by the 3K CMB]

Observations:

1)

There is a difference in sign between preferred and corrected redshifts. A blue shift suggesting motion toward Earth is rare. In this book's data set, 24 galaxies have a negative velocity, or less than 4%.

Calculating V from corrected Z (which is positive) and c is 144 km/s

The V result matches NED V in sign and value.

2)

Calculating D from NED preferred V and H0 is 2.123894 Mpc

The D result is about 26% higher than NED

3)
 From Wikipedia:
V = 144 km/s
D = 1.86 Mpc

Wikipedia V matches NED V
But D values differ

From NED Distances (74):

There are 22 results for Method Cepheids (not all fit in the screen capture).

Their average = 1.945

There are also results from other methods (not all fit in the screen capture).

The D provided by NED is not just from this set.

Wikipedia does not match NED.

From NED Spectra (3):

Here are all of them:

Image 1, Far-Infrared band, from Nucleus region.

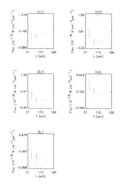

Image 2, H I, from integrated region.

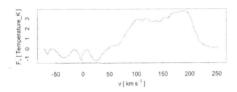

Image 3, H I, from Nucleus region.

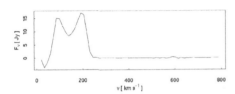

Observations:

Image 1)

This range of wavelengths offers nothing of interest here.

Images 2 and 3)

They have different units for their vertical axis.

Image 2 must be the source of the negative velocity.

There is no spectrum provided for these images plotting velocities, in X, in reference to different types of values, in Y.

The only possible origin of image 3 is some number of emission lines around 21 cm. Each line had its wavelength measured compared to 21 cm. The difference was used to get z where diff / 21 cm = z. Next, each z was multiplied by c, resulting in a series of velocity and wavelength intensity as shown.

It is impossible for this set of atoms in the line of sight, having differences in their 21 cm emission line to indicate the galaxy's proper velocity.

None of these peaks can be the galaxy's velocity in any direction. Using them is a mistake.

It is impossible to measure any 3-dimensional proper velocity when using only the line of sight.

NGC 300 has an unjustified velocity and NED indicates it is somehow measured as a positive or negative z.
The correct value is the statement: there has been no attempt to measure this galaxy's proper velocity.

NGC 300 has a wrong velocity when derived from atoms.

It is impossible to calculate the V/D ratio, or Hubble's constant, for this galaxy.

8.10 NGC 1365

NGC 1365 is in the constellation Leo, in sky quadrant NQ2
Fornax, in sky quadrant SQ1.

From NED Redshifts (61):

Preferred Redshift: Z = 0.00546, H0 = 67.8 km/sec/Mpc, Ω matter = 0.308, Ω vacuum = 0.692

V (Heliocentric) is 1636 ± 1 km/s

Hubble Flow Distance and Distance Modulus (where H0 = 67.8 km/sec/Mpc ± km/sec/Mpc)

D (Local Group) = 22.19 ± 1.56 Mpc

Cosmology-Corrected Quantities [H0 = 67.8 km/sec/Mpc, Ω matter = 0.308, Ω vacuum = 0.692]

[Redshift 0.005133 as corrected to the Reference Frame defined by the 3K CMB]

Observations:

1)
Calculating V from preferred Z and c is 1638 km/s
The V result difference of 2 km/s is trivial.

2)
Calculating D with NED preferred V and H0 is
24.15929 Mpc
The D result is about 9% higher than NED

3)
From Wikipedia:
V = 1636 km/s
D = 17.2 Mpc

Wikipedia V matches NED V
But D values differ

From NED Distances (66):

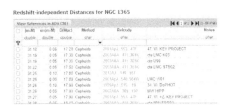

There are 31 results for Method Cepheids (not all fit in the screen capture).

Their average = 18.9533

There are more results from other methods (not all fit in the screen capture).

The D provided by NED is not just from this set.

Wikipedia D does not match NED.

From NED Spectra (24):

Here are the relevant images:

Image 1, Far-IR band, from Integrated region.

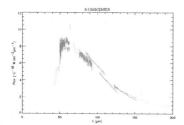

N1365CENTER

Image 2, N III line, from Nucleus region.

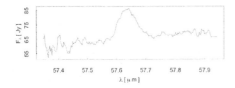

There is another NIII capture, then other metallic lines, including O I, O III, C II.
More spectra are not relevant.

Image 3, H I, from Integrated region.

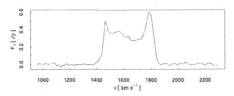

Image 4, H I, from Integrated region.

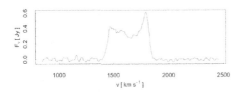

Image 5, H I, from Integrated region.

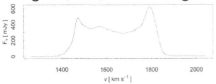

Image 6, H I, from Integrated region.

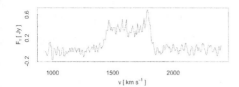

Image 7, Optical band, from Nucleus region.

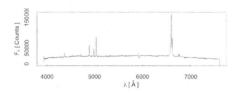

Observations:

Image 1)

This range of wavelengths offers nothing of interest here.

Image 2)

Metallic emission lines from ions in the line of sight indicate nothing of the galaxy.

Images 3-6)

There is no spectrum provided for each plot of velocities. The only possible origin of this plot is some number of emission lines around 21 cm. Each line had its wavelength measured from 21 cm. The difference was compared to 21 cm where diff / 21 cm = z. Next, each z was multiplied by c, resulting in a series of a velocity with wavelength intensity as shown.

No peaks in the neutral hydrogen emissions can be the galaxy's velocity in any direction. Using them is a mistake.

It is impossible for this set of atoms in the line of sight, having differences in their 21 cm emission line, to indicate the galaxy's proper velocity.

Image 7)

6563 A is the Balmer-alpha emission line, and it seems to be captured by this sample. The line suggests a slow proton captured a slow electron, emitting less energy than the Lyman-alpha line, when the atom dropped to ground state, resulting in little or no shift of the line.

This line should be ignored, as it was, because it indicates nothing of the galaxy.

It is impossible to measure any 3-dimensional proper velocity when using only the line of sight.

NGC 1365 has an unjustified non-zero velocity when derived from atoms.

This exercise requires measuring motion in all directions including transverse. It is a mistake of negligence when measuring only in the line of sight.

The velocity measurement requires many positions recorded over a span of time. This is how we measure the motion of comets and asteroids. Galaxies are more distant and require more time because the angular distance covered in time decreases as the distance increases, for the same velocity.

NGC 1365 should have a published statement which directly states there is a range of possible distances. The value must state the uncertainty which is demonstrated by the many different possible values coming from different attempts. A distance being derived from 31 or more values should not omit the uncertainty.

NGC 1365 has a wrong velocity when derived from atoms.

It is impossible to calculate the V/D ratio, or Hubble's constant, for this galaxy.

8.11 NGC 3621

NGC 3621 is in the constellation Hydra, in sky quadrant SQ2.

From NED Redshifts (18):

Preferred Redshift: $Z = 0.00244$, $H0 = 67.8$ km/sec/Mpc, Ω matter $= 0.308$, Ω vacuum $= 0.692$

V (Heliocentric) is 730 ± 2 km/s

Hubble Flow Distance and Distance Modulus (where $H0 = 67.8$ km/sec/Mpc $\pm$ km/sec/Mpc)

D (Local Group) = 6.49 ± 0.52 Mpc

Cosmology-Corrected Quantities [$H0 = 67.8$ km/sec/Mpc, Ω matter $= 0.308$, Ω vacuum $= 0.692$]

[Redshift 0.003548 as corrected to the Reference Frame defined by the 3K CMB]

Observations:

1)
Calculating V from Z and c is 732 km/s
The V result difference of 2 km/s is trivial.

2)
Calculating D from NED preferred V and H0 = 10.79646 Mpc
The D result is about 66% higher than NED

3)

From Wikipedia:
V = 727 km/s
D = 6.64 Mpc

Wikipedia V matches NED V
But D values differ

From NED Distances (47):

There are 22 results for Method Cepheids (not all fit in the screen capture).

Their average = 6.59545

There are more results from other methods (not all fit in the screen capture).

The D provided by NED is not just from this set.

Wikipedia does not match NED.

From NED Spectra (22):

Here are the relevant ones:

Image 1, Optical band, from Nucleus region.

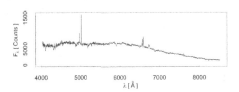

Image 2 and more, Mid-IR band, from Nucleus region.

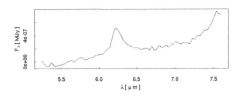

Image 3 and more, O I, from Nucleus region.

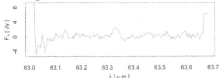

There are more images of metallic ion lines, Including O III, N II, C II. More spectra are not relevant.

Image 4, H I, from Integrated region.

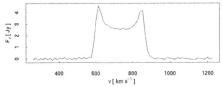

Image 5, H I, from integrated region.

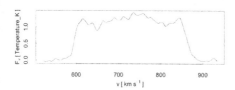

There is also another H I spectrum.

Observations:

Image 1)

There are several emission lines from several ions. They were also captured in other images.

6563 A is the Balmer-alpha emission line, and it seems to be captured by this sample. The line suggests a slow proton captured a slow electron, emitting less energy than the Lyman-alpha line, when the atom dropped to ground state, resulting in little or no shift of the line.

This line should be ignored, as it was, because it indicates nothing of the galaxy.

Image 2)

There is no spectrum provided for this plot of velocities. The only possible origin of this plot is several emission lines around 21 cm. Each line had its wavelength measured from 21 cm. The difference was compared to 21 cm where diff / 21 cm = z. Next, each z was multiplied by c, resulting in a series of a velocity with wavelength intensity as shown.

It is impossible for this set of atoms in the line of sight, having differences in their 21 cm emission line to indicate the galaxy's proper velocity.

The velocity of 732 might come from image 5 not 4. This is not a valid method of measuring a galaxy's velocity. The astronomer is probably unaware that no lines of any origin can indicate the velocity of a galaxy in the line of sight through that atom.

None of these peaks can be the galaxy's velocity in any direction. Using them is a mistake.

It is impossible to measure any 3-dimensional proper velocity when using only the line of sight.

NGC 3621 has an unjustified non-zero velocity.

This exercise requires measuring motion in all directions including transverse. It is a mistake of negligence when measuring only in the line of sight. The velocity measurement requires many positions recorded over a span of time. This is how we measure the motion of comets and asteroids. Galaxies are more distant and require more time because the angular distance covered in time decreases as the distance increases, for the same velocity.

NGC 3621 has a wrong velocity when derived from atoms.

It is impossible to calculate the V/D ratio, or Hubble's constant, for this galaxy.

8.12 NGC 5236

NGC 5236 is also known as M83, and is in the constellation Hydra, in sky quadrant SQ2.

From NED Redshifts (31):

Preferred Redshift: Z = 0.00171, H0 = 67.8 km/sec/Mpc, Ω matter = 0.308, Ω vacuum = 0.692
V (Heliocentric) is 513 ± 2 km/s

Hubble Flow Distance and Distance Modulus (where H0 = 67.8 km/sec/Mpc ± km/sec/Mpc)

D (Local Group) = 4.44 ± 0.36 Mpc

Cosmology-Corrected Quantities [H0 = 67.8 km/sec/Mpc, Ω matter = 0.308, Ω vacuum = 0.692]

[Redshift 0.002645 as corrected to the Reference Frame defined by the 3K CMB]

Observations:

1)
Calculating V from Preferred Z and c is 513 km/s
The V result matches NED.

2)
Calculating D from NED preferred V and H0 = 7.566372 Mpc
The D result is about 70% more than NED

Calculating D from NED corrected Z to get a corrected V (793.5) and with H0 = 11.70354 Mpc

This is even higher than using preferred Z, so a larger difference.

3)
 From Wikipedia:
V = 508 km/s
D = 4.5 Mpc

Wikipedia V matches NED V
But D values differ, with preferred z, or corrected z.

From NED Distances:

There are 2 results for Method Cepheids (both are in the screen capture)
Their average = 4.555

There are 8 results from other methods, after those in the image above (not all fit in the screen capture).

With the 8 methods shown in the image, and 8 seen after scrolling and so all 16 methods are visible.

NED does not identify the final distance value, after considering the set of 16 values available by scrolling this page in NED.

The origin of the distance value from NED is not clear from
 This display page in NED.

Wikipedia D does not match NED.

From NED Spectra (22):

Here are the relevant ones:

Image 1, Optical band, from Nucleus region.

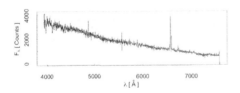

Image 2, UV band, from Nucleus region.

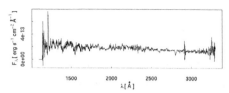

Image 3, H I, from integrated region.

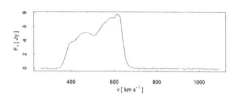

Image 4, Mid-IR, from integrated region.

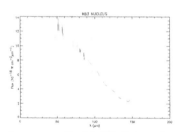

Image 5, N III line, from Integrated region.

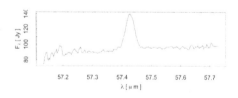

There are more spectra of metallic ion emissions, including O I, O III, N II, O I; some have more than 1 image. More spectra are not relevant.

Observations:

Image 1)

There are several emission lines near the infrared end.

Image 2)

Lyman-alpha emission line was detected in UV band. It appears close to 1216 A, so the proton was not moving fast, at the moment of its electron capture.

This event detection has nothing to do with a galaxy's velocity or distance.

Image 3)

This distribution must be the origin of the velocity.

There is no spectrum provided for this plot of velocities. The only possible origin of this plot is several emission lines around 21 cm. Each line had its wavelength measured from 21 cm. The difference was compared to 21 cm where diff / 21 cm = z. Next, each z was multiplied by c, resulting in a series of velocity with wavelength intensity as shown.

It is impossible for this set of atoms in the line of sight, having differences in their 21 cm emission line to indicate the galaxy's proper velocity.

Image 4)

This infrared band offers nothing of interest here. NGC 5236 has an unjustified non-zero velocity when based on atoms.

This exercise requires measuring motion in all directions including transverse. It is a mistake of negligence when measuring only in the line of sight. The velocity measurement requires many positions recorded over a span of time. This is how we measure the motion of comets and asteroids. Galaxies are more distant and require more time because the angular distance covered in time decreases as the distance increases, for the same velocity.

NGC 5236 has a wrong velocity when derived from atoms.

It is impossible to calculate the V/D ratio, or Hubble's constant, for this galaxy.

8.13 NGC 4038

NGC 4038, is also known as one of the Antennae galaxy pair, and is in the constellation Corvus, in sky quadrant SQ3.

From NED Redshifts (22):

Preferred Redshift: $Z = 0.00548$, $H0 = 67.8$ km/sec/Mpc, Ω matter = 0.308, Ω vacuum = 0.692

V (Heliocentric) is 1642 ± 12 km/s

Hubble Flow Distance and Distance Modulus (where $H0 = 67.8$ km/sec/Mpc $\pm$ km/sec/Mpc)

D (Local Group) = 20.67 ± 1.47 Mpc

Cosmology-Corrected Quantities [$H0 = 67.8$ km/sec/Mpc, Ω matter = 0.308, Ω vacuum = 0.692]

[Redshift 0.006661 as corrected to the Reference Frame defined by the 3K CMB]

Observations:

1)
Calculating V from preferred Z and c is 1644 km/s
The V result difference of 2 km/s is trivial.

2)
Calculating D from NED V and H0 is
24.24779 Mpc
The D result is about 17% higher than NED

3)
 From Wikipedia:
V = 1642 km/s
D = 19.94 Mpc

Wikipedia V matches NED V
But D values differ

From NED Distances (27):

There are 3 results for Method Cepheids (all are in the screen capture)

Their average = 20.0

There are more results from other methods (not all fit in the screen capture).

The D provided by NED is not just from this set.

Wikipedia does not match NED.

From NED Spectra (3):

Here are the images:

Image 1, Far-IR band, from Nucleus region.

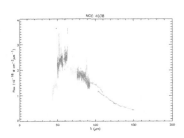

Image 2, H I, from integrated region.

Image 3, H I, from integrated region.

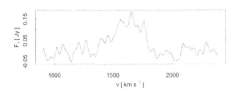

Observations:

Image 1)

This infrared band offers nothing of interest here.

Images 2 and 3)

Image 3 not 2 is probably the origin of the velocity. NED never explicitly identifies the spectrum for a velocity value.

There is no spectrum provided for these plots of velocities. The only possible origin of this plot is a several emission lines around 21 cm. Each line had its wavelength measured from 21 cm. The difference was compared to 21 cm where diff / 21 cm = z. Next, each z was multiplied by c, resulting in a series of a velocity with wavelength intensity as shown.

It is impossible for this set of atoms in the line of sight, having differences in their 21 cm emission line to indicate the galaxy's proper velocity.

None of these peaks can be the galaxy's velocity in any direction. Using them is a mistake.

It is impossible to measure any 3-dimensional proper velocity when using only the line of sight.

NGC 4038 has an unjustified non-zero velocity. The correct value is the statement: there has been no attempt to measure this galaxy's proper velocity.

This exercise requires measuring motion in all directions including transverse. It is a mistake of negligence when measuring only in the line of sight. The velocity measurement requires many positions recorded over a span of time. This is how we measure the motion of comets and asteroids. Galaxies are more distant and require more time because the angular distance covered in time decreases as the distance increases, for the same velocity.

NGC 4038 has a wrong velocity when derived from atoms.

It is impossible to calculate the V/D ratio, or Hubble's constant, for this galaxy.

8.14 NGC 5128

NGC 5128 is also known as Centaurus A, is in the constellation Centaurus, in sky quadrant SQ3.

From NED Redshifts (58):

Preferred Redshift: Z = 0.00183, H0 = 67.8 km/sec/Mpc, Ω matter = 0.308, Ω vacuum = 0.692

V (Heliocentric) is 547 ± 5 km/s

Hubble Flow Distance and Distance Modulus (where H0 = 67.8 km/sec/Mpc ± km/sec/Mpc)

D (Local Group) = 4.44 ± 0.39 Mpc

Cosmology-Corrected Quantities [H0 = 67.8 km/sec/Mpc, Ω matter = 0.308, Ω vacuum = 0.692]

[Redshift 0.002678 as corrected to the Reference Frame defined by the 3K CMB]

Observations:

1)
Calculating V from preferred Z and c is 549 km/s
The V result difference of 2 km/s is trivial.

2)
Calculating D from NED V and H0 is 8.097345 Mpc
The D result is about 82% higher than NED

3)
From Wikipedia:
V = 547 km/s
D = about 4 Mpc

Wikipedia V matches NED V
But D values differ by about 11%

From NED Distances (54):

Redshift-independent Distances for NGC 5128

There are 4 results for Method Cepheids (all are in the screen capture)

Their average = 3.27

There are more results from other methods (not all fit in the screen capture).

The D provided by NED is not just from this set.

Wikipedia does not match NED.

From NED Spectra (23):

Here are the relevant ones:

Image 1, Far-IR band, from Nucleus region.

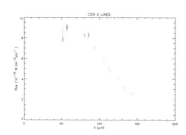

Image 2, O III line at 52 um, from Nucleus region.

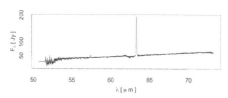

Image 3, O I line at 63 um, from Nucleus region.

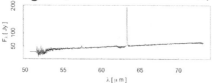

There are more spectra with metallic ion emission lines, including O I, N II, N III, C II; with some repeated. More spectra are not relevant.

Image 4, H I, from integrated region.

Observations:

Image 1)

There is nothing of interest in this band of long wavelengths.

Images 2-3)

Metallic ion emission lines arise in the line of sight and indicate nothing of the galaxy

Image 4)

There is no spectrum provided for this plot of velocities. The only possible origin of this plot is a several emission lines around 21 cm. Each line had its wavelength measured from 21 cm. The difference was compared to 21 cm where diff / 21 cm = z. Next, each z was multiplied by c, resulting in a series of a velocity with wavelength intensity as shown.
It is impossible for this set of atoms in the line of sight, having differences in their 21 cm emission line, to indicate the galaxy's proper velocity.

This somewhat random distribution is apparently the origin of the redshift velocity.

None of these peaks can be the galaxy's velocity in any direction. Using them is a mistake.

It is impossible to measure any 3-dimensional proper velocity when using only the line of sight.

NGC 5128 has an unjustified non-zero velocity when derived from atoms.

This exercise requires measuring motion in all directions including transverse. It is a mistake of negligence when measuring only in the line of sight. The velocity measurement requires many positions recorded over a span of time. This is how we measure the motion of comets and asteroids. Galaxies are more distant and require more time because the angular distance covered in time decreases as the distance increases, for the same velocity.

NGC 5128 should have a published statement which directly states there is a range of possible distances. The value must state the uncertainty which is demonstrated by the many different possible values coming from different attempts. A distance being derived from 7 or more values should not omit the uncertainty.

NGC 5128 has a wrong velocity when derived from atoms.

It is impossible to calculate the V/D ratio, or Hubble's constant, for this galaxy.

8.15 NGC 5253

NGC 5253 is in the constellation Centaurus, in sky quadrant SQ3.

From NED Redshifts (25):

Preferred Redshift: $Z = 0.00136$, H0 = 67.8 km/sec/Mpc, Ω matter = 0.308, Ω vacuum = 0.692

V (Heliocentric) is 407 ± 3 km/s

Hubble Flow Distance and Distance Modulus (where H0 = 67.8 km/sec/Mpc ± km/sec/Mpc)

D (Local Group) = 2.85 ± 0.28 Mpc

Cosmology-Corrected Quantities [H0 = 67.8 km/sec/Mpc, Ω matter = 0.308, Ω vacuum = 0.692]

[Redshift 0.002272 as corrected to the Reference Frame defined by the 3K CMB]

Observations:

1)
Calculating V from preferred Z and c is 408 km/s
The V result difference of 1 km/s is trivial.

2)
Calculating D from NED preferred V and H0 is
6.017699 Mpc
The D result is more than 2 times that from NED

3)
 From Wikipedia:
V = 407 km/s
D = 3.33 Mpc

Wikipedia V matches NED V
But D values differ, with W higher

From NED Distances (55):

There are 26 results for Method Cepheids (not all fit in the screen capture).

Their average = 3.9156

There are more results from other methods (not all fit in the screen capture).

The D provided by NED is not just from this set.

Wikipedia does not match NED.

From NED Spectra (6):

Here are the images:

Image 1, UV band, from Nucleus region.

Image 2, Optical band, from Nucleus region.

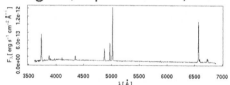

Image 3, H I, from integrated region.

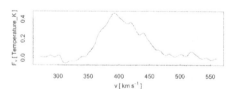

Image 4, H I, from integrated region.

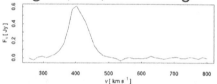

Image 5, H I, from integrated region.

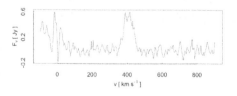

Image 6, Optical band, from integrated region.

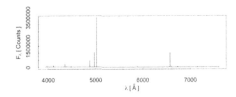

Observations:

Image 1)

Lyman-alpha emission line was detected in UV band. It appears close to 1216 A, so it was not moving fast at the moment of electron capture.

This event detection has nothing to do with a galaxy's velocity or distance.

Images 2, 6)

These metallic ion emission lines arise in the line of sight, and indicate nothing of the galaxy.

Images 3, 4, 5)

There is no spectrum provided for each plot of velocities. The only possible origin of this plot is a several emission lines around 21 cm. Each line had its wavelength measured from 21 cm. The difference was compared to 21 cm where diff / 21 cm = z. Next, each z was multiplied by c, resulting in a series of velocity with wavelength intensity as shown.

It is impossible for this set of atoms in the line of sight, having differences in their 21 cm emission line to indicate the galaxy's proper velocity.

None of them seem to show 407, the claimed velocity.

None of these peaks can be the galaxy's velocity in any direction. Using them is a mistake.

It is impossible to measure any 3-dimensional proper velocity when using only the line of sight.

NGC 5253 has an unjustified non-zero velocity when derived from atoms.

This exercise requires measuring motion in all directions including transverse. It is a mistake of negligence when measuring only in the line of sight. The velocity measurement requires many positions recorded over a span of time. This is how we measure the motion of comets and asteroids. Galaxies are more distant and require more time because the angular distance covered in time decreases as the distance increases, for the same velocity.

NGC 5253 has a wrong velocity when derived from atoms.

It is impossible to calculate the V/D ratio, or Hubble's constant, for this galaxy.

8.16 NGC 4535

NGC 4535 is in the constellation Virgo, in sky quadrant SQ3.

From NED Redshifts (30):

Preferred Redshift: $Z = 0.00655$, H0 = 67.8 km/sec/Mpc, Ω matter = 0.308, Ω vacuum = 0.692

V (Heliocentric) is 1964 ± 1 km/s

Hubble Flow Distance and Distance Modulus (where H0 = 67.8 km/sec/Mpc ± km/sec/Mpc)

D (Local Group) = 27.19 ± 1.91 Mpc

Cosmology-Corrected Quantities [H0 = 67.8 km/sec/Mpc, Ω matter = 0.308, Ω vacuum = 0.692]

[Redshift 0.007668 as corrected to the Reference Frame defined by the 3K CMB]

Observations:

1)
Calculating V from preferred Z and c is 1965 km/s
The V result difference of 1 km/s is trivial.

2)
Calculating D from NED using preferred V and H0 is 28.9823 Mpc
The D result is about 7% higher than D from NED.

3)

From Wikipedia:
V = 1962 km/s
D = 16.6 Mpc

Wikipedia V is near NED V
But D values differ

From NED Distances (54):

Redshift-independent Distances for NGC 4535

(m-M)	err(m-M)	D(Mpc)	Method	Refcode	
double	double	double	char	char	
30.86	0.05	14.88	Cepheids	2001ApJ..553..47P	47, VI, KEY PROJECT
30.87	0.07	14.96	Cepheids	2002A&A..389..19P	MW HIPP
30.87	0.05	15.00	Cepheids	2003A&A..411..361K	cte LMC K03
30.88	0.06	15.00	Cepheids	2001ApJ..548..68AW	LMC W01
30.88	0.05	15.00	Cepheids	2003A&A..411..361K	cte U99
30.91	0.06	15.23	Cepheids	2003A&A..411..361K	cte LMC-STS02
30.97	0.05	15.63	Cepheids	2003A&A..411..361K	cte MW FS(07)
30.98	0.20	15.70	Cepheids	2002A&A..389..19P	MW P02
30.99	0.05	15.80	Cepheids	2001ApJ..553..47P	47, VI, +Z, KEY PROJEC
31.00	0.05	15.90	Cepheids	2003A&A..411..361K	cte MF91
31.02	0.05	16.00	Cepheids	2003A&A..411..361K	cte MW GFG50
31.08	0.07	16.40	Cepheids	2002A&A..383..3502	54, VI

There are 19 results for Method Cepheids (not all fit in the screen capture).

Their average = 16.28

There are more results from other methods (not all fit in the screen capture).

The D provided by NED is not just from this set.

Wikipedia D does not match NED.

From NED Spectra (5):

Here are the 5 images:

Image 1, H I line, from integrated region.

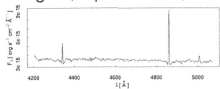

Image 2, Optical band, from Nucleus region.

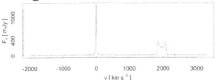

Image 3, Optical band, from Nucleus region.

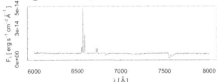

Image 4, Optical band, from Nucleus region.

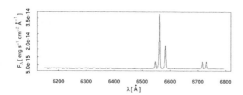

Image 5, H I, from integrated region.

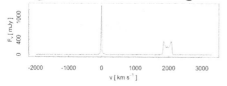

Observations:

Images 1 and 5)

There is no spectrum provided for these plots of velocities. The only possible origin of this plot is several emission lines around 21 cm. Each line had its wavelength measured from 21 cm. The difference was compared to 21 cm where diff / 21 cm = z. Next, each z was multiplied by c, resulting in a series of velocity with wavelength intensity as shown.

It is impossible for this set of atoms in the line of sight, having differences in their 21 cm emission line to indicate the galaxy's proper velocity.

There is a peak near 1962, which is the stated velocity.

However, both images show zero velocity as the strongest line. A case could be made for zero velocity for this galaxy.

When one line shows apparent motion while another line shows none, then this is definitely not a consistent measurement.

None of these peaks can be the galaxy's velocity in any direction. Using them is a mistake.

It is impossible to measure any 3-dimensional proper velocity when using only the line of sight.

NGC 4535 has an unjustified non-zero velocity.

This exercise requires measuring motion in all directions including transverse. It is a mistake of negligence when measuring only in the line of sight. The velocity measurement requires many positions recorded over a span of time. This is how we measure the motion of comets and asteroids. Galaxies are more distant and require more time because the angular distance covered in time decreases as the distance increases, for the same velocity.

NGC 4535 has a wrong velocity, when based on atoms in the line of sight.

It is impossible to calculate the V/D ratio, or Hubble's constant, for this galaxy.

8.17 NGC 4536

NGC 4536 is in the constellation Virgo, in sky quadrant SQ3

From NED Redshifts (33):

Preferred Redshift: Z = 0.00603, H0 = 67.8 km/sec/Mpc, Ω matter = 0.308, Ω vacuum = 0.692

V (Heliocentric) is 1808 ± 1 km/s

Hubble Flow Distance and Distance Modulus (where H0 = 67.8 km/sec/Mpc ± km/sec/Mpc)

D (Local Group) = 24.51 ± 1.72 Mpc

Cosmology-Corrected Quantities [H0 = 67.8 km/sec/Mpc, Ω matter = 0.308, Ω vacuum = 0.692]

[Redshift 0.007174 as corrected to the Reference Frame defined by the 3K CMB]

Observations:

1)
Calculating V from preferred Z and c is 1809 km/s
The V result difference of 1 km/s is trivial.

2)
Calculating D from NED V and H0 is
26.68142 Mpc
The D result is about 9% higher than NED

3)

From Wikipedia:
V = 1808 km/s
D = 14.9 Mpc

Wikipedia V matches NED V
But D values differ

From NED Distances (84):

Redshift-independent Distances for NGC 4536

There are 28 results for Method Cepheids

Their average = 15.613158

There are more results from other methods (not all fit in the screen capture).

The D provided by NED is not just from this set.

Wikipedia does not match NED.

From NED Spectra (27):

Here are the relevant ones:

Image 1, Mid-IR Band, from Nucleus region.

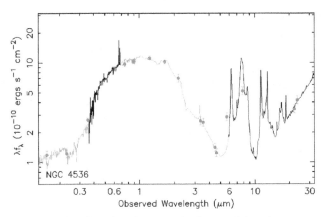

Image 2, Optical band, from Nucleus region.

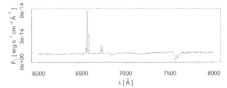

Image 3, O I, from integrated region.

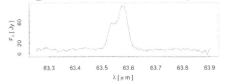

Images 4, 5, 17 are also O I.

Images 6-8 are, O III, from integrated region.

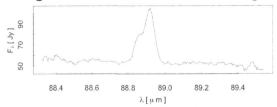

Images 9 – 14 are N II, C II, with some repeating.

Image 15, H I, from integrated region.

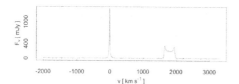

Image 16, H I, from integrated region.

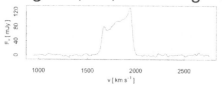

Observations:

Image 1)

This band of long wavelengths offers nothing important.

Image 2 indicates several absorption and emission lines. They arise from atoms in the line of sight and indicate nothing of the galaxy.

Images 15, 16)

There is no spectrum provided for these plots of velocities. The only possible origin of this plot is several emission lines around 21 cm. Each line had its wavelength measured from 21 cm. The difference was compared to 21 cm where diff / 21 cm = z.
Next, each z was multiplied by c, resulting in a series of velocity with wavelength intensity as shown.

Image 16 might be the origin of the claimed velocity.

It is impossible for this set of atoms in the line of sight, having differences in their 21 cm emission line to indicate the galaxy's proper velocity.

None of these peaks can be the galaxy's velocity in any direction. Using them is a mistake.

It is impossible to measure any 3-dimensional proper velocity when using only the line of sight.

NGC 4536 has an unjustified non-zero velocity when derived from atoms.

This exercise requires measuring motion in all directions including transverse. It is a mistake of negligence when measuring only in the line of sight. The velocity measurement requires many positions recorded over a span of time. This is how we measure the motion of comets and asteroids. Galaxies are more distant and require more time because the angular distance covered in time decreases as the distance increases, for the same velocity.

NGC 4536 has a wrong velocity when derived from atoms.

It is impossible to calculate the V/D ratio, or Hubble's constant, for this galaxy.

8.18 Cepheid Summary

Only 17 galaxies beyond our Local Group have Cepheids in them.

Noting all their redshifts are from emission lines finds no acceptable velocity when calculating the ratio of the correct galaxy's velocity to its distance.
None of these galaxies having Cepheids can provide a valid result for a possible value for Hubble's constant.

Cosmology cannot have any important constant dependent on a galaxy's velocity. No galaxy has a correctly measured velocity.

9 Quasars

Quasar is short for quasi-stellar object. They are faint in visual wavelengths, by dimming from clouds of ions, but intense in a wide range of wavelength from X-ray to radio. A quasar is misunderstood in modern cosmology.

My model for a quasar was presented in my book Cosmology Transition, but its details are not relevant to this book about redshifts. The same rule for a galaxy redshift applies to a quasar.
Neither has a physical surface, like a photosphere for attaching an atom. Therefore, no atoms can move with the quasar. All absorption lines (quasars exhibit none) and all emission lines exhibit nothing about a quasar's motion.

The spectrum of a quasar has many emission lines. Arp did not do an analysis of a quasar's redshift mechanism, but I did. His book offered 2 annotated spectrograms. Unknown to Arp, a quasar actually has 2 measurable red shifts:

1) Hydrogen Lyman-alpha emission line; this occurs when a proton captures an electron; the change in the new hydrogen atom's energy state is radiated away in this wavelength; the velocity or kinetic energy of the proton at that instant results in a redshift of that wavelength.
This emission line is found in a typical quasar and is its primary red shift measurement. There are quasars with this line red shifted indicating a proton velocity more than 6 times the velocity of light, when the quasar z is greater than 6.

2) Emission lines from a number of metallic ions, where metallic means not hydrogen or helium.

These emission lines occur when an ion captures an electron; the change in the ion's energy state is radiated away in this wavelength; the ion's velocity, relative to the velocity of light at that instant, results in a red shift of that characteristic wavelength. All the ions share the same red shift because all are moving by the electrical charge differential with the plasmoid in the quasar's core.

The variety of metallic ions can vary among quasars from different Seyferts.

A Seyfert galaxy is in a galaxy class called LINER, for Low-Ionization Nuclear Emission Region.[R201]

When a Seyfert ejects a plasmoid from its core, the plasmoid is accompanied by the mix of metal ions in this particular Seyfert. The ejection mechanism is not relevant to this book.

The Seyfert provides the ions which are observed by the second red shift.

A plasmoid is a torus-shaped plasma entity having an electrical current bound by its magnetic field. A plasmoid was famously imaged in April 2019 in the core of M87 galaxy. [R201]

The plasmoid and the M87 jets were explained in a YouTube video titled: "Wal Thornhill: Black Hole or Plasmoid?"

For an immediate reference for a quasar spectrum, here is a figure from a Caltech web article describing a typical quasar spectrum, including its caption. [R202]

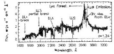

Figure 1. Typical spectrum of a quasar, showing the quasar continuum and emission lines, and the absorption lines produced by galaxies and intergalactic material that lie between the quasar and the observer. This spectrum of the $z = 1.34$ quasar PKS0454−039 was obtained with the Faint Object Spectrograph on the Hubble Space Telescope. The emission lines at ~ 2400 Å and ~ 2850 Å are Lyβ and Lyα. The Lyα forest, absorption produced by various intergalactic clouds, is apparent at wavelengths blueward of the Lyα emission line. The two strongest absorbers, due to galaxies, are a damped Lyα absorber at $z = 0.86$ and a Lyman limit system at $z = 1.15$. The former produces a Lyman limit break at ~ 1700 Å and the latter a partial Lyman limit break at ~ 1950 Å since the neutral Hydrogen column density is not large enough for it to absorb all ionizing photons. Many absorption lines are produced by the DLA at $z = 0.86$ (C IV λλ1548, for example, is redshifted onto the red wing of the quasar's Lyα emission line).

The figure shows the measured wavelength of redshifted "Lya Emission" from the "z=1.34"

This "typical quasar" is superluminal, with z >1.

However, this redshift velocity is of the proton, not the quasar.

The caption has "quasar continuum and emission lines" where "continuum" is its synchrotron radiation from its AGN, which is a plasmoid, and the spectrogram shows many emission lines from metallic ions capturing ions. The caption finishes with the "quasar's Lya emission line, separate from the rest.

The Lyman-alpha emitter description in the section Galaxies implied this line occurs under extreme conditions, while here a typical quasar will exhibit this line. Typical is not extreme.

The comparison suggests the LAE galaxy description was written when unaware of typical quasars.

The very important conclusion with quasars is their red shift always comes from emission lines, which always come from either an ion or proton capturing an electron. Emission lines offer no information, like velocity, of any object behind them in the line of sight.

9.1 Mechanism for a superluminal proton.

The video referenced above described how the plasmoid in M87 emits jets having a high velocity.

With F_D meaning duration of force

From basic physics, $F = ma$
$V = a * F_D$

Therefore, a sustained force will achieve a velocity based on mass and duration.

A plasmoid is an electric current bound by the magnetic field being generated, so it is an electrical ring. In the center of that ring is a magnetic field, as well as on the outside of the ring. A positively charged proton moving through the center of the ring is subject to the Lorentz force which acts at a perpendicular angle, so the proton is accelerated by this force and its final velocity depends on the duration of its presence in the field and on its strength. Einstein had a wrong assumption that mass has a velocity limit at c. That is a mistake shown by a typical quasar.

Note:

Einstein's wrong assumption has interesting consequences.

When a force is sustained, then the energy is being transferred to kinetic energy in the mass. If the mass does not increase its velocity, then either the energy must be transferred to another object, or it is lost which is a violation of thermodynamics and the conservation of energy. Einstein was wrong.

10 Cosmic Distance Ladder

Astronomers have several methods for determining the distance to a galaxy. This begins the topic. Several subsequent sections cover specific methods.

The cosmic distance ladder (also known as the extragalactic distance scale) is the succession of methods by which astronomers determine the distances to celestial objects. A real direct distance measurement of an astronomical object is possible only for those objects that are "close enough" (within about a thousand parsecs) to Earth. The techniques for determining distances to more distant objects are all based on various measured correlations between methods that work at close distances and methods that work at larger distances. Several methods rely on a standard candle, which is an astronomical object that has a known luminosity.

Almost all astronomical objects used as physical distance indicators belong to a class that has a known brightness. By comparing this known luminosity to an object's observed brightness, the distance to the object can be computed using the inverse-square law. These objects of known brightness are termed standard candles, coined by Henrietta Swan Leavitt.

Two problems exist for any class of standard candle. The principal one is calibration, that is the determination of exactly what the absolute magnitude of the candle is. This includes defining the class well enough that members can be recognized, and finding enough members of that class with well-known distances to allow their true absolute magnitude to be determined with enough accuracy. The second problem lies in recognizing members of the class, and not mistakenly using a standard candle calibration on an object which does not belong to the class. At extreme distances, which is where one most wishes to use a distance indicator, this recognition problem can be quite serious.

A significant issue with standard candles is the recurring question of how standard they are. For example, all observations seem to indicate that Type Ia supernovae that are of known distance have the same brightness (corrected by the shape of the light curve). The basis for this closeness in brightness is discussed below; however, the possibility exists that the distant Type Ia supernovae have different properties than nearby Type Ia supernovae. The use of Type Ia supernovae is crucial in determining the correct cosmological model. If indeed the properties of Type Ia supernovae are different at large distances, i.e. if the extrapolation of their calibration to arbitrary distances is not valid, ignoring this variation can dangerously bias the reconstruction of the cosmological parameters, in particular the reconstruction of the matter density parameter.

That this is not merely a philosophical issue can be seen from the history of distance measurements using Cepheid variables.

In the 1950s, Walter Baade discovered that the nearby Cepheid variables used to calibrate the standard candle were of a different type than the ones used to measure distances to nearby galaxies. The nearby Cepheid variables were population I stars with much higher metal content than the distant population II stars.

As a result, the population II stars were actually much brighter than believed, and when corrected, this had the effect of doubling the distances to the globular clusters, the nearby galaxies, and the diameter of the Milky Way. [R207]

Observation:

The problems with assigning stars to 1 of the 3 populations were explained in section Star Types.

Walter Baade's discovery is crucial. Hubble's Law was based on relating distances obtained from Cepheids with the measured redshift values of galaxies. The method of measuring each value is important.

The method of measuring the redshift of each galaxy, with or without a Cepheid, is very important.

This book has a section Galaxies with Cepheids.

Several other methods can be immediately discarded.

One is the "standard siren" which is based on a claimed sound extracted from gravitational waves. My book, Predicting Gravitational Wave Detections, described how to predict GW detections by LIGO. This prediction reveals LIGO's deception of declaring a GW detection during specific lunar and solar events. LIGO is an abomination for proper science.

There is no such thing as a gravitational wave, so there can be no standard siren based on that mistake.

A second questionable method uses a supernova.

The often-cited study which claimed to find consistent supernovae, enabling them to be a candidate for a standard candle, was riddled with errors. The most important mistake is the study used variable stars, not supernovae.

The study included a chart of their consistent light curves which never had an extreme brightening which should be a requirement for a claimed supernova. The mistake was confirmed within the paper by including one example of the star's spectrum and its change during the event. The change was consistent with that expected in a Cepheid-type variable star. The dimming of the claimed supernovae was also consistent with a Cepheid.

A supernova is expected to shed mass during the explosive event. That significant change makes it rather unlikely for these extreme events to follow the same luminosity curve. A Cepheid's slow brightening in the course of its light curve spanning a few days is not like a supernova, which abruptly increases in brightness by many magnitudes.
Each supernova is a unique event and is not a candidate for a standard candle.

The Cosmic Distance Ladder continues:

The following four indicators all use stars in the old stellar populations (Population II):

- Tip of the red-giant branch (TRGB) distance indicator.
- Planetary nebula luminosity function (PNLF)
- Globular cluster luminosity function (GCLF)
- Surface brightness fluctuation (SBF)

[R250]

Observation:
Each of the 4 will be addressed in section NED Distances.

11 NED Redshifts

NED identifies different redshift measurements.

11.1 Photometric Red Shift

Photometric redshift is a measurement which is not based on a shift of a specific absorption or emission line, obtained by analysis using spectroscopy.

Observation:
This method is inconsistent with the Doppler Effect cases described in the last section.

A photometric redshift is an estimate for the recession velocity of an astronomical object such as a galaxy or quasar, made without measuring its spectrum.
The technique uses photometry (that is, the brightness of the object viewed through various standard filters, each of which lets through a relatively broad passband of colours, such as red light, green light, or blue light) to determine the redshift, and hence, through Hubble's law, the distance, of the observed object.

The technique was developed in the 1960s, but was largely replaced in the 1970s and 1980s by spectroscopic redshifts, using spectroscopy to observe the frequency (or wavelength) of characteristic spectral lines, and measure the shift of these lines from their laboratory positions.

The photometric redshift technique has come back into mainstream use since 2000, as a result of large sky surveys conducted in the late 1990s and 2000s which have detected a large number of faint high-redshift objects, and telescope time limitations mean that only a small fraction of these can be observed by spectroscopy. Photometric redshifts were originally determined by calculating the expected observed data from a known emission spectrum at a range of redshifts. The technique relies upon the spectrum of radiation being emitted by the object having strong features that can be detected by the relatively crude filters.

As photometric filters are sensitive to a range of wavelengths, and the technique relies on making many assumptions about the nature of the spectrum at the light-source, errors for these sorts of measurements can range up to $\delta z = 0.5$, and are much less reliable than spectroscopic determinations. In the absence of sufficient telescope time to determine a spectroscopic redshift for each object, the technique of photometric redshifts provides a method to determine an at least qualitative characterization of a redshift.

For example, if a Sun-like spectrum had a redshift of $z = 1$, it would be brightest in the infrared rather than at the yellow-green color associated with the peak of its blackbody spectrum, and the light intensity will be reduced in the filter by a factor of two (i.e. $1+z$) (see K correction for more details on the photometric consequences of redshift). [R2211]

The most important assumption when using this method is there are "strong features that can be detected by the relatively crude filters."

When there are no strong features, this method cannot provide a valid result.

Unfortunately, galaxy spectra being synchrotron radiation lack strong features.
The description mentions a "Sun-like spectrum" but that is not correct for a galaxy.

Perhaps, this method could work with stars. Their spectrum is from thermal radiation, so it has a "strong feature" because the wavelength having the highest intensity is associated with the light source temperature. The solar spectrum was provided in the section Stars.

When trying to apply this method to galaxies, the result might be like finding a pattern in noise.

11.2 Galaxy examples.

There are no readily available examples of specific galaxies and their spectra which passed through this specific processing. When lacking other's data, this book can provide real data to illustrate this exercise.

There are 2 spiral galaxy spectra in section Galaxy Types, with M31 and M33 but they used Cepheids for their distance.

There are also spectra of 17 galaxies in the section Cepheids.

None of these galaxies exhibit a "strong feature" to be affected by color filters as described.

The synchrotron radiation will exhibit no strong features like a star's spectrum can. Galaxies might have an emission line but whether it falls into a range of a filter could be random. An emission line comes from an atom and its motion, and is not valid for a massive galaxy.

11.3 Student Exercise

Someone from Rice University posted an Astronomy Laboratory exercise in 2014. A link is not included because the details of the specific exercise are not important. Its title is (if some wants to read it):[R213]

Measuring the Redshift of M104 – The Sombrero Galaxy.

As an exercise, it might be purged and disappear from the internet eventually.

None of this description is about anything the student did. This is about the exercise and the analysis being done by software.

The student is given a spectrogram of M104 galaxy and the M104 measurements:
M104 z = 0.00342 and its velocity = 1024 km/sec.

The M104 spectrogram shows wavelengths from about 3900 Angstroms to 7200.

The student apparently has access to software which can identify lines from Mercury and Neon.
The software apparently calculates the z and velocity for these lines.

The software used these metallic lines to calculate a velocity which was off from expected for M104 by 68%.

The student is not learning where the M104 velocity came from.

Among the many mistakes the student might not recognize:

1) The spectrogram does not present the origin of the stated velocity.

2) Mercury and neon lines are always irrelevant to a galaxy. They are atoms in the line of sight and any measured motion is irrelevant. If the results had been closer than off by 68%, the results are still meaningless.

The inappropriate spectrogram cannot reveal the spectrum an astronomer must have used for the M104 value, which is identified below after checking the set of 25.

I did an exercise a student might have to do, finding the origin of the accepted velocity of M104.

The PDF has references, including NED.

The following are the spectra in NED for M104. There are 25 in the set. The origin of the M104 velocity is not in the spectrogram given to the student.

The NED spectra at the time of writing this did not include the spectra in the exercise, despite 25 in the set.

Image 1, from the integration of multiple telescopes, in the UV-Mid-IR band.

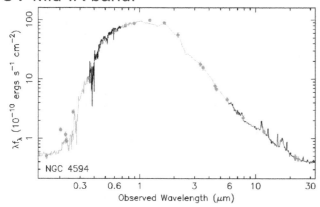

Image 2 is the UV band from the Nucleus Region.

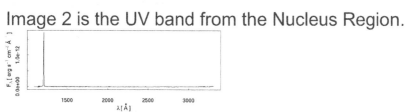

Image 3 is the Optical band from the Nucleus Region.

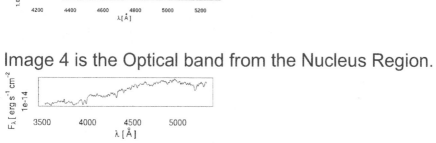

Image 4 is the Optical band from the Nucleus Region.

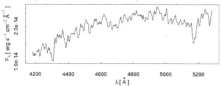

Image 5 is the Optical band from the Nucleus Region.

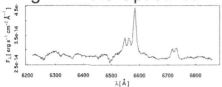

Image 6 is the Near-IR band from the Nucleus Region.

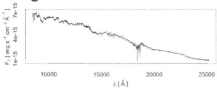

Image 7 is the Mid-IR band from the Nucleus Region.

Image 8 is the Mid-IR band from the Nucleus Region.

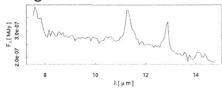

Image 9 is the Mid-IR band from the Nucleus Region.

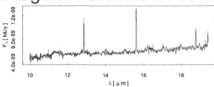

Image 10 is the Mid-IR band from the Nucleus Region.

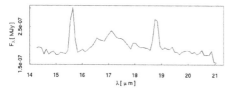

Image 11 is the Mid-IR band from the Nucleus Region.

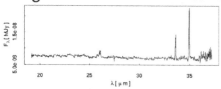

Image 12 is the Mid-IR band from the Nucleus Region.

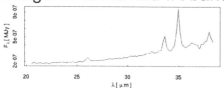

Image 13 is the [OI] 63μm line from the Nucleus Region.

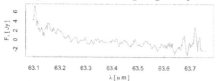

Images 14 and 15 are also O I.

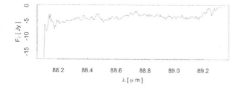

Images 16 and 17 are [OIII] 88µm line from the Nucleus Region.

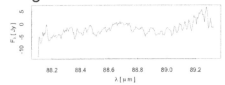

Images 18, 19, 20, 21 are [NII] 122µm line from the Nucleus Region.

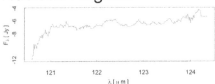

Images 22, 23, 24 are [CII] 158µm line from the Nucleus Region.

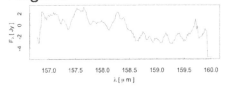

Image 25 is H I from Integrated Region.

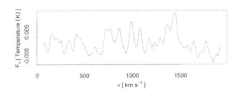

Observations:

Image 1)

The long wavelengths in this infrared band offer nothing of interest here.

Image 2)

Lyman-alpha emission line was detected in UV band. It appears close to 1216 A, so it was not moving fast at the moment of electron capture.

This line detection has nothing to do with a galaxy's velocity or distance.

Images 3, 4, 5)

There are candidate absorption and emission lines in the optical wavelength band. Some of the Balmer series lines are in this range. If any of them are shifted, these atoms are in the line of sight and indicate nothing of the galaxy.

Images 6-12)

There is nothing if interest for a galaxy in these mid-infrared wavelengths.

Images 13-24)

These are spectrum captures of the galactic nucleus.

The nucleus of the Sombrero Galaxy is classified as a low-ionization nuclear emission-line region (LINER).

A LINER galaxy is characterized by metallic emission lines.

These spectra of various elements (there are several for different elements) are worthless, when trying to measure a galaxy's velocity or distance. These atoms are in motion within the nucleus. It is a mistake to assume any motion they might have, in this narrow region, is at all related to the much larger galaxy.

There is no spectrum provided for these plots of velocities. The only possible origin of this plot is several emission lines around 21 cm. Each line had its wavelength measured from 21 cm. The difference was compared to 21 cm where diff / 21 cm = z. Next, each z was multiplied by c, resulting in a series of velocity with wavelength intensity as shown.

Image 25 might be the origin of the claimed velocity of 1024.

The first peak is around 1000 while the second could be around 1024.

Taking one peak out of a distribution is not a suitable measurement technique. In this case, the selected value must have a defined margin of error to address the inherent uncertainty in the mix when using this method.

If the student had been given this spectrum in place of the one in the exercise, they would have confronted the clear ambiguity when using the neutral hydrogen emission line.

Perhaps the exercise was just for the calculations, not to learn how the velocity is extracted from a measurement, like an astronomer must do.
It is impossible for this set of atoms in the line of sight, having differences in their 21 cm emission line to indicate the galaxy's proper velocity.

None of these peaks can be the galaxy's velocity in any direction. Using them is a mistake.

It is impossible to measure any 3-dimensional proper velocity when using only the line of sight.

11.4 Negative velocity

There at least 20 galaxies having a negative relative velocity in the data set.

These are unusual because in most cases, the atoms are moving toward the galaxy by gravity, not away.

The 2 close spiral galaxies in our Local Group are M31 and M33. As noted in Section Galaxyies, their negative velocity comes from the calcium ion absorption lines, which arise in the line of sight, not the galaxy. The optical spectra from both were provided.

It is a mistake to measure a shift of an absorption or emission line in a galaxy spectrum, and then use that shift from an atom as a velocity for the galaxy.

From the Data Set, these are the other galaxies having a negative velocity:

Segue 2 dwarf, Ursa Minor dwarf, Pisces dwarf,

IC 10, IC 1613, Maffei 2, WLM,
NGC 147, 185, 221, 404, 598, 3031, 4192, 4569, 6166, 6822.

12 NED Distances

NED identifies galaxies using specific distance calculation methods: Tully-Fisher Relation, Faber-Jackson Relation

Both SDSS and Wikipedia offer an overview of photometric Redshifts. [R222]

Each of the NED functions has its detailed explanation below.

12.1 Tully-Fisher Relation

The Tully-Fisher Relation attempts to calculate a galaxy's distance based on several assumptions with luminosity.

The Tully–Fisher relation (TFR) is an empirical relationship between the mass or intrinsic luminosity of a spiral galaxy and its asymptotic rotation velocity or emission line width. It was first published in 1977 by astronomers R. Brent Tully and J. Richard Fisher. The luminosity is calculated by multiplying the galaxy's apparent brightness by $4\pi d^2$ is its distance from us, and the spectral-line width is measured using long-slit spectroscopy.

Several different forms of the TFR exist, depending on which precise measures of mass, luminosity or rotation velocity one takes it to relate. Tully and Fisher used optical luminosity, but subsequent work showed the relation to be tighter when defined using microwave to infrared (K band) radiation (a good proxy for stellar mass), and even tighter when luminosity is replaced by the galaxy's total baryonic mass (the sum of its mass in stars and gas). This latter form of the relation is known as the Baryonic Tully–Fisher relation (BTFR), and states that baryonic mass is proportional to velocity to the power of roughly 3.5–4.

The TFR can be used to estimate the distance to spiral galaxies by allowing the luminosity of a galaxy to be derived from its directly measurable line width. The distance can then be found by comparing the luminosity to the apparent brightness. Thus the TFR constitutes a rung of the cosmic distance ladder, where it is calibrated using more direct distance measurement techniques and used in turn to calibrate methods extending to larger distance.

In the dark matter paradigm, a galaxy's rotation velocity (and hence line width) is primarily determined by the mass of the dark matter halo in which it lives, making the TFR a manifestation of the connection between visible and dark matter mass. In Modified Newtonian dynamics (MOND), the BTFR (with power-law index exactly 4) is a direct consequence of the gravitational force law effective at low acceleration.

The analogues of the TFR for non-rotationally-supported galaxies, such as ellipticals, are known as the Faber–Jackson relation and the fundamental plane. [R224]

Observation:

There is a fundamental wrong assumption here.

Stars in galaxies of any type are not moving by the force of gravity.
It is impossible for only the attractive force of gravity to explain stellar motion in spiral galaxies.

There is no justification for this assumption when there are only a few planets orbiting within a similar plane (some planets have slightly inclined orbits) around a much more massive single star. The Sun and planets move around the system's center of gravity in elliptical orbits. A galactic disk has billions of stars with clouds of gas and dust, within several arms. A spiral galaxy also has a bulge having many stars distributed within a sphere. The bulge is nothing like a single star to compare to the Sun and solar system. Our Sun is thought to move in a roughly circular orbit, but its orbit is considered disturbed by the millions of other stars also in the disk. Stars have a net positive charge which enables their motion to be driven by the Lorentz force from a spiral galaxy's magnetic field. Spiral galaxies with their bulge and arms do not resemble the solar system.

Several of these galaxies, including our Milky Way, have a bar between the galactic core and the start of the arms. Our solar system has nothing like spiral arms.

Gravity must have a diminished, to negligible, role in a spiral galaxy.

The rotation of the M31 disk was explained by its magnetic field by astronomers in Spain, in 2010. No dark matter is needed when this cause explains the rotation. [R226]

A study of spiral galaxy IC342 concluded its magnetic fields explain the structure of the spiral arms, not gravity. [R226]

Dark matter is needed as an excuse when magnetic fields are ignored.

When TFR has an explicitly stated connection to non-existent dark matter, then TFR is connected to a mistake.

12.2 Galaxy example: NGC 4535.

The following images are from NED, or the NASA Extragalactic Database.

NGC 4535 has Cepheids so some of its data, including spectra, are in section Cepheids. The top of the Distances (54) list was shown. Several of the Cepheid distances were shown.
Only the average of all the Cepheid distances was shown in that section.

Here is a lower segment of that display, where Tully-Fisher distances begin

Here is the bottom segment of that display, where the Tully-Fisher distances end.

Here, the critical line on the display of 54 values is this excerpt with its distance:

16.10 Mpc | Statistical Method | Note: Mean of Cepheids and Tully-Fisher

According to this line, NED calculated the mean of many values with the result of 16.10 Mpc.
For comparison, the NED redshift distance using the redshift velocity and H0 is 27.19 Mpc

This redshift distance is 69% higher than statistical mean of distances using Cepheids and using TFR.

The problem is: there is no impartial distance measurement serving as the benchmark to check values from the respective methods, like Redshift, TFR, and Cepheids.

12.3 Faber-Jackson Relation

The Faber–Jackson relation provided the first empirical power-law relation between the luminosity and the central stellar velocity dispersion of elliptical galaxy, and was presented by the astronomers Sandra M. Faber and Robert Earl Jackson in 1976. [R229]

Observation:

The term "velocity dispersion" should be defined here.

"In astronomy, the velocity dispersion (σ) is the statistical dispersion of velocities about the mean velocity for a group of astronomical objects, such as an open cluster, globular cluster, galaxy, galaxy cluster, or supercluster. By measuring the radial velocities of the group's members through astronomical spectroscopy, the velocity dispersion of that group can be estimated and used to derive the group's mass from the virial theorem. Radial velocity is found by measuring the Doppler width of spectral lines of a collection of objects; the more radial velocities one measures, the more accurately one knows their dispersion. A central velocity dispersion refers to the σ of the interior regions of an extended object, such as a galaxy or cluster.
The relationship between velocity dispersion and matter (or the observed electromagnetic radiation emitted by this matter) takes several forms in astronomy based on the object(s) being observed.

For instance, the Faber–Jackson relation for elliptical galaxies, and the Tully–Fisher relation for spiral galaxies. For example, the σ found for objects about the Milky Way's supermassive black hole (SMBH) is about 75 km/s. The Andromeda Galaxy (Messier 31) hosts a SMBH about 10 times larger than our own, and has a σ ≈ 160 km/s. [R230]

Observation:

There is a wrong fundamental assumption here.

Stars in galaxies of any type are not moving by the force of gravity.
Stars have a net positive charge. That enables stars to move by the Lorentz force from a spiral galaxy's magnetic field. This was explained in the TRF description earlier, with citations.

Instead of accepting the 2010 study of M31, and admitting there is no dark matter, as clamed, cosmology continues with the discredited dark matter excuse, because they consistently ignore electromagnetism.

The recognition that stars have a positive charge is important to elliptical galaxies also.

In an elliptical galaxy, the stars are moving by electrodynamics, the mechanism for charged bodies in motion. The details are not crucial here, other than noting gravity is wrong for galaxies, by many reasons, including dropping any mention of dark matter.

Cosmology invokes dark matter whenever a magnetic field is ignored so an unexpected behavior has no explanation using gravity. That mistake results in gravity being invoked first, leading to dark matter.

The description of this method mentions the velocity dispersion in the elliptical galaxy.

I checked Wikipedia for details of all elliptical galaxies in the Messier list: M49, M87, M89, M105, and M110. Wikipedia offers extensive descriptions, but none of the galaxies have their velocity dispersion.

It is impossible to review this method when the proposed algorithm has no supporting data or examples of its actual application.

12.4 Branch Methods

Horizontal Branch, Tip of Red Giant Branch, and Red Clump are described.

12.4.1 Horizontal Branch

Horizontal Branch is another method of estimating a galaxy's distance without a detailed analysis of lines in its spectrum.

The horizontal branch (HB) is a stage of stellar evolution that immediately follows the red giant branch in stars whose masses are similar to the Sun's. Horizontal-branch stars are powered by helium fusion in the core (via the triple-alpha process) and by hydrogen fusion (via the CNO cycle) in a shell surrounding the core. The onset of core helium fusion at the tip of the red giant branch causes substantial changes in stellar structure, resulting in an overall reduction in luminosity, some contraction of the stellar envelope, and the surface reaching higher temperatures.

Horizontal branch stars were discovered with the first deep photographic photometric studies of globular clusters and were notable for being absent from all open clusters that had been studied up to that time. The horizontal branch is so named because in low-metallicity star collections like globular clusters, HB stars lie along a roughly horizontal line in a Hertzsprung–Russell diagram. Because the stars of one globular cluster are all at essentially the same distance from us, their apparent magnitudes all have the same relationship to their absolute magnitudes, and thus absolute-magnitude-related properties are plainly visible on an H-R diagram confined to stars of that cluster, undiffused by distance and thence magnitude uncertainties. [R233]

Observation:

The application of this method requires:

a) Resolution to individual stars in the galaxy,
b) Certainty in identifying the type of star being measured,

c) the life cycle of a star is not certain since one cycle has never been observed, so any assumptions based on are invalid; the description is not clear on this dependence.

With current imaging technology, this method could be limited for application at distances far beyond the Local Group.

12.4.2 Tip of the red-giant branch (TRGB) distance indicator

Tip of the red-giant branch (TRGB) is a primary distance indicator used in astronomy.

It uses the luminosity of the brightest red-giant-branch stars in a galaxy as a standard candle to gauge the distance to that galaxy. It has been used in conjunction with observations from the Hubble Space Telescope to determine the relative motions of the Local Cluster of galaxies within the Local Supercluster. Ground-based, 8-meter-class telescopes like the VLT are also able to measure the TRGB distance within reasonable observation times in the local universe. [R235]

Observation:

The application of this method requires:

a) Resolution to individual stars in the galaxy,
b) Certainty in identifying the type of star being measured,

12.4.3 Red Clump

Red Clump is another method of estimating a galaxy's distance without a detailed analysis of lines in its spectrum.

The red clump is a clustering of red giants in the Hertzsprung–Russell diagram at around 5,000 K and absolute magnitude (MV) +0.5, slightly hotter than most red-giant-branch stars of the same luminosity. It is visible as a denser region of the red-giant branch or a bulge towards hotter temperatures. It is prominent in many galactic open clusters, and it is also noticeable in many intermediate-age globular clusters and in nearby field stars (e.g. the Hipparcos stars). [R235]

Observation:

The application of this method requires:

a) Resolution to individual stars in the galaxy,
b) Certainty in identifying the type of star being measured,

With current imaging technology, this method could be too limited for application at distances far beyond the Local Group. The description suggests it works only to Hipparcos distances.

12.5 Luminosity Methods

The luminosity methods are: Luminosity distance, PNLF, GCLF, and SBF, CMD. Each method is described here.

12.5.1 Luminosity Distance

Luminosity Distance is another method of estimating a galaxy's distance without a detailed analysis of lines in its spectrum.

Luminosity distance D_L is defined in terms of the relationship between the absolute magnitude M and apparent magnitude m of an astronomical object.

$$M = m - 5(\log_{10}D_L - 1)$$
which gives:

$$D_L = 10^{(m-M)+1}$$

where D_L is measured in parsecs. For nearby objects (say, in the Milky Way) the luminosity distance gives a good approximation to the natural notion of distance in Euclidean space.

The relation is less clear for distant objects like quasars far beyond the Milky Way since the apparent magnitude is affected by spacetime curvature, redshift, and time dilation. Calculating the relation between the apparent and actual luminosity of an object requires taking all of these factors into account.

The object's actual luminosity is determined using the inverse-square law and the proportions of the object's apparent distance and luminosity distance.
Another way to express the luminosity distance is through the flux-luminosity relationship. Since,

$$F = L / (4\pi D_L^2)$$

where F is flux ($W \cdot m^{-2}$), and L is luminosity (W). From this the luminosity distance can be expressed as:

$$D_L = \text{square root of } (L / 4\pi F)$$

The luminosity distance is related to the "comoving transverse distance" by

$$D_L = (1 + z) D_M$$

And with the angular distance parameter D_A by the Etherington's reciprocity theorem:

$$D_L = (1 + z)^2 D_A$$

where z is the redshift. is a factor that allows calculation of the comoving distance between two objects with the same redshift but at different positions of the sky; if the two objects are separated by an angle $\delta\theta$. the comoving distance between them would be $D_M \delta\theta$. In a spatially flat universe, the comoving transverse is exactly equal to the radial comoving D_C, i.e. the comoving distance from ourselves to the object. [R238]

Observation:

There are many false assumptions in this method so one must doubt its results.

1) One mistake is the claim: "the apparent magnitude is affected by spacetime curvature, redshift, and time dilation"

None of those things affects magnitude. Curvature and time dilation cannot apply here because they can apply only to the special moving observer. All celestial objects move only according to the sum of all forces acting on them. None move according to the rules applied by space-time.

Therefore, the universe is "spatially flat" so Euclidean space is the correct context, just like for near objects.

A galaxy redshift is only a measured change in a specific emission line wavelength, so it is impossible to affect the magnitude of the full spectrum.

12.5.2 Planetary nebula luminosity function (PNLF)

Planetary nebula luminosity function (PNLF) is a secondary distance indicator used in astronomy. It makes use of the [O III] λ5007 forbidden line found in all planetary nebula (PNe) which are members of the old stellar populations (Population II). It can be used to determine distances to both spiral and elliptical galaxies despite their completely different stellar populations and is part of the Extragalactic Distance Scale.

The relative independence of the PNLF cutoff with respect to population age is harder to understand. The [O III] λ5007 flux of a PNe directly correlates to the brightness of its central star. Further, the brightness of its central star directly correlates to its mass and the central star's mass directly varies in relation to its progenitor's mass. However, by observation, it is demonstrated that reduced brightness does not happen. [R240]

Observation:

This "does not happen" because there are too many baseless assumptions. This function depends on correctly understanding a star's life cycle. As mentioned in section Stars, the presence of elements is explained wrong by the defective fusion model. Robitaille's LMH model, without internal fusion under impossible equilibrium, explains all stellar observations. Cosmologists are wrong about the life cycle of a star.
The application of the PNLF method requires:

a) Resolution to individual stars in the galaxy, and even to a rare planetary nebula,

a) Certainty in identifying the type of star being measured for its nebula expected to possess specific elements,
b) Certainty in understanding how, when and why, a star erupts and ejects the plasma shell called a planetary nebula.

Perhaps PNLF can be improved but right now it is invalid simply because of (c); the current gaseous sun model using a fusion cycle is wrong when it fails to explain many solar observations.

However, the Robitaille LMH model for a star matches all solar observations.

Therefore, any conclusions using PNLF will probably be wrong.

12.5.3 Globular cluster luminosity function (GCLF)

A paper was published in 2010 having the title:

Globular cluster luminosity function as distance indicator

Another paper reviewed that paper.

Lately the study of the Globular Cluster Systems has been used more as a tool for galaxy formation and evolution, and less so for distance determinations. [R241]

Observation:

With that published paper stating the limited application of GCLF, any applications of GCLF for a distance will probably be wrong.

12.5.4 Surface brightness fluctuation (SBF)

Surface brightness fluctuation (SBF) is a secondary distance indicator used to estimate distances to galaxies. It is useful to 100 Mpc (parsec). The method measures the variance in a galaxy's light distribution arising from fluctuations in the numbers of and luminosities of individual stars per resolution element.
The SBF technique uses the fact that galaxies are made up of a finite number of stars. The number of stars in any small patch of a galaxy will vary from point to point, creating a noise-like fluctuation in its surface brightness. While the various stars present in a galaxy will cover an enormous range of luminosity, the SBF can be characterized as having an average brightness. A galaxy twice as far away appears twice as smooth as a result of the averaging. Older elliptical galaxies have fairly consistent stellar populations, thus it closely approximates a standard candle. In practice, corrections are required to account for variations in age or metallicity from galaxy to galaxy. Calibration of the method is made empirically from Cepheids or theoretically from stellar population models. [R242]

Observation:

The section Galaxies with Cepheids noted there are few of them. If this function requires a Cepheid, then it is limited to only a few galaxies.
This surface brightness analysis ignores every galaxy has an AGN in its core which is a source of synchrotron radiation extending from X-ray to radio. The visible light from every galaxy has a component from the AGN.

It is quite impossible to have an accurate correction for anything when our history of accumulating data with appropriate precision spans over only decades, while the life cycle of stars is assumed to span millions of years. We have never observed an entire life cycle of any individual star. When lacking a history, any correction is just conjecture.

The life cycle of stars is misunderstood, when based on the internal fusion mechanism. The LMH model explains stars better. Assumptions based on stellar populations lack an acceptable foundation for this SBF to be valid.

The application of the SBF method requires:

a) Resolution to individual stars in the galaxy, and even within an elliptical galaxy where only outer stars on the near side can be measured; its limit at 100 Mpc is acknowledged,

b) Certainty in identifying the type of star being measured which is currently expected to possess specific elements.

Perhaps SBF can be improved but right now it is invalid simply because of (b); the current gaseous sun model using a fusion cycle is wrong when it fails to explain many solar observations.

However, the Robitaille LMH model for a star matches all solar observations.

Therefore, any conclusions using SBF will probably be wrong.

12.5.5 Color-Magnitude Diagram (CMD)

The galaxy color–magnitude diagram shows the relationship between absolute magnitude (a measure of luminosity) and mass of galaxies.

Unlike the comparable Hertzsprung–Russell diagram for stars, galaxy properties are not necessarily completely determined by their location on the color–magnitude diagram. The diagram also shows considerable evolution through time. [R244]

Observation:

The diagram has its x-axis as from low luminosity to high, and y-axis is from red to blue. Red is most ellipticals, while blue is most spirals. Both axes are poorly defined. There is no defined procedure for measuring the mass of a galaxy.

CMD is mentioned for only 6 galaxies in my review of 600+ galaxies in NED.

Perhaps, this function is still being refined for a wider application.

13 Hubble's Law

Hubble's Law describes a mathematical relationship between a galaxy's red shift velocity and its distance.

13.1 Description

Hubble's law, also known as the Hubble–Lemaître law, is the observation in physical cosmology that galaxies are moving away from the Earth at speeds proportional to their distance. In other words, the farther they are the faster they are moving away from Earth. The velocity of the galaxies has been determined by their redshift, a shift of the light they emit toward the red end of the spectrum.

Hubble's law is considered the first observational basis for the expansion of the universe, and today it serves as one of the pieces of evidence most often cited in support of the Big Bang model. The motion of astronomical objects due solely to this expansion is known as the Hubble flow. It is often expressed by the equation $v = H0D$, with $H0$ the constant of proportionality—Hubble constant—between the "proper distance" D to a galaxy, which can change over time, unlike the comoving distance, and its speed of separation v, i.e. the derivative of proper distance with respect to cosmological time coordinate. (See uses of the proper distance for some discussion of the subtleties of this definition of 'velocity'.)

Hubble constant is most frequently quoted in (km/s)/Mpc, thus giving the speed in km/s of a galaxy 1 megaparsec (3.09×10^{19} km) away, and its value is about 70 (km/s)/Mpc. However, the SI unit of H0 is simply s−1, and the SI unit for the reciprocal of H0 is simply the second. The reciprocal of H0 is known as the Hubble time. The Hubble constant can also be interpreted as the relative rate of expansion.

The parameters that appear in Hubble's law, velocities and distances, are not directly measured. [R246]

Observation:

The last sentence in the excerpt clearly identifies the fundamental problem with Hubble's Law.
One must be explicitly clear what exactly IS directly measured. There is only 1 measurement of a galaxy, that of an atom's redshift.
A distance cannot be directly measured.

Only a change in a particular wavelength in a galaxy spectrum from its expected value can be directly measured.

The critical decision is whether the change is only in the atom or also in the galaxy behind it in the line of sight.

The mistake of assigning the atom's velocity to the galaxy has been made consistently for over 100 years.

Any distance cannot be directly measured.
A distance can be calculated based on a few assumptions, such as dimming by distance. This is a simple calculation, but it must have a margin of error based on the reliability of the directly measuring the brightness of both the target object and the benchmark object.

13.2 Background

In 1912, Vesto Slipher measured the first Doppler shift of a "spiral nebula" (spiral nebula is the obsolete term for spiral galaxies), and soon discovered that almost all such nebulae were receding from Earth.
He did not grasp the cosmological implications of this fact, and indeed at the time it was highly controversial whether or not these nebulae were "island universes" outside our Milky Way. [R247]

Edwin Hubble is often incorrectly credited with discovering the redshift of galaxies.
These measurements and their significance were understood before 1917 by James Edward Keeler, Vesto Melvin Slipher, and William Wallace Campbell at other observatories.

Combining his own measurements of galaxy distances with Vesto Slipher's measurements of the redshifts associated with the galaxies, Hubble and Milton Humason discovered a rough proportionality of the objects' distances with their redshifts. [R247]

Observation:

Slipher measured redshifts of atoms, not velocities of galaxies.

13.2 Initial measurements

I can find no record of Slipher's specific redshift galaxies to discover the atoms being used, but several references agree his blue shift galaxy was Andromeda. Since Slipher measured the same velocity as accepted from the calcium atom, so that one atom is known. Unfortunately, this was a blue shift, so it did not conform to Hubble's Law and could not be part of the initial set.

The redshift velocity depends on the particular atom being used by the individual astronomer making the measurement in a spectrum.

The distance should have required a standard candle, like a Cepheid or RR Lyrae. The RR Lyrae cannot be used for distances beyond the Local Group so Hubble could use only galaxies having Cepheids. Lemaître claimed to have a value in 1926 while Hubble had one in 1929.

An article titled "How Hubble Found Distances"
Offers an explanation.

From observations of the apparent magnitudes of the brightest stars in 14 more nebulae, Hubble estimated their distances. Now he could calculate an average absolute magnitude for the brightest stars in all 20 nebulae. Comparing this value with the apparent magnitudes of the stars in four nebulae in the still more distant Virgo Cluster of galaxies, he determined their distance too. [R248]

Observation:
Hubble used a few galaxies with Cepheids to compare their magnitudes with others. He created estimated distances, not measured.

Harvard has a relevant page: THE HUBBLE CONSTANT

It was made possible by in part by Vesto Slipher's measurements of the apparent radial velocities of nebulae, but primarily by Edwin Hubble's estimates of distances to nearby galaxies. Hubble deserves the credit for the discovery of the expansion, even though papers by Georges Lemaitre and H. P. Robertson using Hubble's data on the velocity-distance relation preceded his 1929 landmark, because it was his systematic program of measuring galaxy distances and his 1924 discovery of Cepheid variable stars in M31 and his actual plot of the relation that finally convinced the community at large. Low level controversy ensued almost immediately. [R249]

Observation:

This controversy involved the age of the universe implied by the initial value of Hubble's constant which was only 2Gy, while the Earth was assumed to have an age of 3Gy.

The article has more interesting details, but it also reveals something more important.

This observation with my emphasis is critical when trying to understand the origin of the crisis with the constant.

Slipher measured the velocities while Hubble **estimated** the distances. Others, like Lemaitre and Robertson, were using Hubble's data for their papers.

Hubble **estimated** distances, without a precise measurement.

The essential problem for astronomers is finding an acceptable velocity for an acceptable distance to calculate an acceptable value of Hubble's Constant.

13.3 Recent measurements

There is a 2014 study titled:

"The Most Luminous z= 9-10 Galaxy candidates yet found: The Luminosity Function, Cosmic Star-Formation Rate, And The First Mass Density Estimate At 500 Myr"

Excerpt from this paper about galaxies with z from 9 to 10:

The identification of LBGs in the epoch of reionization makes use of the almost complete absorption of UV photons shortward of the redshifted Ly-alpha line due to a high neutral hydrogen fraction in the inter-galactic medium. [R250]

Observation:

The Lyman-alpha emission line is emitted when a proton captures an electron becoming a hydrogen atom. The velocity and direction of the proton at the instant of captures causes a shift in this characteristic wavelength.

These galaxies are not moving at z from 9 to 10, because the extreme red shift is from the high velocity proton, not a velocity of the galaxy.

As noted in this book's introduction:

In my opinion, one's first response to any value of z>1 should be:

"This superluminal velocity is impossible for a massive galaxy, so its measurement must be a mistake."

13.4 Consistency

The study of high redshift galaxies confirmed the red shifted Ly-alpha line is being used for the measured redshift value.

This line is emitted when a proton in the line of sight captures an electron. The velocity of the proton at that instant shifts the wavelength. Therefore, the high red shift galaxies have a high red shift mechanism unlike other galaxies using the neutral hydrogen emission line for the wrong velocity.

Inconsistent methods of measurement result in inconsistent comparison of values. Comparing values from different lines can be misleading. This study found the protons moving toward these galaxies had similar velocities, for the group to be measured in the range of z = 9 to 10.

However, any absorption or emission lines cannot be applied to a galaxy's velocity.

The galaxies in the survey were not identified. NED did not have an entry for the long galaxy names being assigned to these special galaxies. In other words, they do not have NGC numbers, at the time that I compiled the data.

Hubble's Law was based on the shift of the absorption or emission lines noted by the astronomer for that particular galaxy. Currently, astronomers can use whatever lines are found in a star's spectrum, so astronomers measure galaxies just like stars.

13.5 Lateral motion

Astronomers had never attempted to measure a galaxy's lateral motion, not just a Doppler driven velocity in the line of sight, until recently.

The two Magellanic Clouds are galaxies close to our Milky Way, but their far Southern position inhibits viewing by Northern telescopes.

Announced in 2006, measurements with the Hubble Space Telescope suggest the Large and Small Magellanic Clouds may be moving too fast to be orbiting the Milky Way.
In 2014, measurements from the Hubble Space Telescope made it possible to determine that the LMC has a rotation period of 250 million years. [R253]

From this news story about this measurement:

" CfA reveals Magellanic Clouds are first-time visitors"

Earlier this year, CfA astronomers reported measuring the 3-D velocities of the Magellanic Clouds through space with greater accuracy than ever before. The velocities were anomalously high. Two explanations were proposed: 1) the Milky Way is more massive than previously thought, or 2) the Magellanic Clouds are not gravitationally bound to the Milky Way. Further analysis by Besla and her colleagues verified the second explanation. The parabolic orbit they calculated for the clouds, based on the observed velocities, shows that both are on their first pass by the Milky Way. [R253]

Observation:

It is ironic there are only 2 galaxies in the universe having an attempt to measure a 3-D velocity, and both were fast in passing, when the unjustified assumption using Doppler effect is all galaxies have no lateral motion.

All other galaxies, lacking any attempt to measure any such motion, are just assumed to have motion only in the direction of their line of sight from Earth.

13.6 Definition of Hubble's Constant

Descriptions of this constant indicate its value is misunderstood.

The Hubble constant has been interpreted as the relative rate of expansion.

Hubble's Law is based on a ratio's numerator being a consistent motion of atoms toward the galaxy in the line of sight, but this motion is treated as the galaxy's velocity. This redshift has nothing to do with a fictitious expansion. When the atoms move in proportion to distance, this is the result of these atoms interacting with light and plasma within the space between galaxies, called the intergalactic medium, or IGM. Light having energy of ultraviolet or higher can ionize matter

The ratio's denominator is the galaxy's distance. Cepheids are a distance benchmark because a decrease in expected brightness can be attributed to dimming by a specific distance, so a Cepheid in the galaxy could provide this value for its host galaxy. A Cepheid is called a standard candle because it has a predictable luminosity curve, enabling the dimming by distance calculation.

A Cepheid distance measurement establishes the denominator for the ratio or relationship of Velocity divided by Distance
This ratio applies to its host galaxy and is assumed applicable to other galaxies with a uniform expansion. Currently, there is no other reliable alternative to a Cepheid.

Everything dims by distance. Stars require instruments having very high resolution to measure individual stars among the billions in a galaxy. Efforts to use the known luminosity of certain bright, giant stars also encounter this limitation.

Supernovae were also candidates for a standard candle. I did a detailed analysis of the study using supernovae to justify the false expansion, and it was riddled by many errors including mistakes with redshifts. The supernovae had a luminosity curve like a variable star. The spectrum of a supposed supernova matched that of a variable star. The change in spectrum during the change in luminosity was claimed to be a redshift. This study is worthless. Supernovae are not consistent, as they must be to qualify as a possible benchmark.

13.6 Consequences of Hubble's Law

When astronomers get a redshift. A distance can be calculated.
When astronomers get a distance, like from a Cepheid in a galaxy, a velocity can be calculated. That is an unjustified uniform and consistent universe.
Astronomers formed invalid conclusions using this law.

An earlier reference included:

"Hubble's law is considered the first observational basis for the expansion of the universe, and today it serves as one of the pieces of evidence most often cited in support of the Big Bang model. "

This claim of evidence is quite unjustified.

Currently, all galaxies and quasars have invalid velocities.

There are no galaxies having a correctly measured velocity.

Therefore, Hubble's Law and its assumed relationship between redshift velocity and distance are invalid.

Therefore, there is no observational evidence supporting a big bang theory based on all distant galaxies in recession while all have invalid velocities, while having no attempt to measure the proper motion, independent of Earth, of any galaxy.

14 Hubble's Constant

14.1 Constant ratio in uniform geocentric universe

Hubble's constant by its 2 factors, velocity and distance, implicitly defines a geocentric universe having uniform behaviors of all its galaxies, where a velocity relative to Earth cannot vary by galaxy and where a distance from Earth cannot vary by galaxy.

14.2 Calculating the ratio

The method of using a Cepheid for calculating a value for Hubble's Constant was described in section Hubble's Law.

Cosmologists are trying other methods. In 2017, Astronomy magazine posted this article: [R260]

HOLiCOW! Astronomers measuring the expansion of the universe confirm that we still don't understand everything

Rather than copying or paraphrasing, several of the organized attempts at measuring Hubble's Constant are described by their advocates in the article.

The project trying to use the CMB will fail because the CMB does not exist. Dr Robitaille explained these instruments are detecting the molecular vibrations of water in Earth's oceans, not the CMB. The map of the CMB looks like noise because it is just a map of noise from Earth's oceans.

The galaxy names and their data in NED are required to see their spectra for independent analysis of the studies.

There are scenarios where an agreement on a value is impossible.
 a) Cosmologists develop accurate distance metrics based on luminosity,
 b) The mix of galaxies in the study are using varying atoms, like neutral hydrogen or absorption lines or emission lines. These lines determine a velocity. These lines cannot affect luminosity. The atoms will probably have inconsistent velocities.
 c)
 d) Some type of luminosity metric like a Cepheid will determine a distance. Luminosity cannot affect the atoms in the line of sight. One exception is where UV from an energetic galaxy can ionize the neutral atoms.
The universe really cannot be driven by us on Earth, where a galaxy's distance from Earth is related by a simple ratio to the galaxy's velocity relative to Earth.

Around the celestial sphere, there could be several galaxies at about the same distance from Earth. Depending on the individual galaxy, the atoms in the line of sight appearing in its spectrum could vary. The simplest scenario is many galaxies can share the neutral hydrogen line where each galaxy attracts by gravity these atoms. If at that distance around the celestial sphere, a LINER galaxy is included then its metallic emission lines will have a galaxy dependent velocity. The V/D ratio will be inconsistent. Hubble's constant assumes all galaxies have the same redshift mechanism. This is wrong, making an agreement on Hubble's constant impossible.

15 Charts

The methods identified in NED for specific galaxies are charted. These methods were explained in previous sections. The methods used by the respective galaxies are plotted in charts.

15.1 Possible redshifts identified in NED spectra

An astronomer can select a shifted emission or absorption line based on a seriously bad assumption. These lines are always from atoms in the line of sight, so it is literally impossible for any of them to indicate a 3-dimensional velocity of the galaxy behind it, in the line of sight.

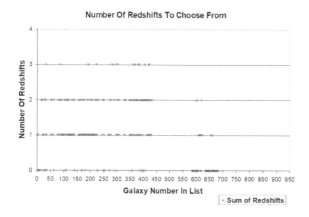

When the spectrum contains no prominent absorption or emission lines, then the astronomer must use one of the distance calculations, based on luminosity. Those are the marks on the zero line.

Perhaps, a chart of each line per galaxy could be presented. This could add 1 page per line. It is easier for only the person interested to view the galaxy spreadsheet in the Data Set.

15.2 Using the H I line from neutral hydrogen

This emission line applies to only an atom and cannot indicate a galaxy's velocity. Unfortunately, many galaxies have that mistake.

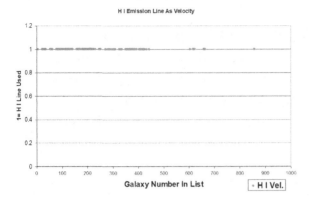

15.3 Using a metallic emission line

An emission line, from an atom in the line of sight, cannot indicate a galaxy's velocity. Unfortunately, many galaxies could have that mistake.

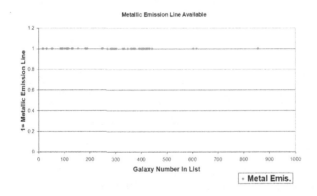

The most distant galaxies lack a spectrum but have only a measured magnitude, which can be used to estimate its distance.

15.4 Distance Methods

An astronomer has several methods which are available to calculate a distance when having no redshift. NED, in its Distances tab, identifies the methods being used.

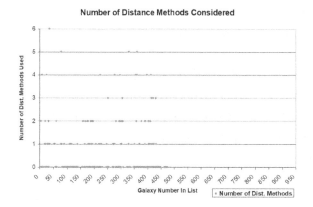

Number of Distance Methods Considered

Perhaps, a chart of each method per galaxy could be presented. This could add 1 page per method. It is easier for the person interested to view the galaxy spreadsheet in the Data Set.

16 Big Bang

The big bang theory arose after many galaxies were measured having a red shift. The theory's history and future are discussed.

16.1 Origin

The philosophy of Aristotle held that the universe had an infinite past, which caused problems for medieval Jewish and Islamic philosophers who were unable to reconcile the Aristotelian conception of the eternal with the Abrahamic view of creation.

Observationally, in the 1910s, Vesto Slipher and later, Carl Wilhelm Wirtz, determined that most spiral nebulae (now correctly called spiral galaxies) were receding from Earth.

In 1927, the Belgian Catholic priest Georges Lemaitre proposed an expanding model for the universe to explain the observed redshifts of spiral nebulae, and calculated the Hubble law. He based his theory on the work of Einstein and De Sitter, and independently derived Friedmann's equations for an expanding universe. Also, the red shifts themselves were not constant, but varied in such manner as to lead to the conclusion that there was a definite relationship between amount of red-shift of nebulae, and their distance from observers.

In 1931, Lemaître proposed in his "hypothèse de l'atome primitif" (hypothesis of the primeval atom) that the universe began with the "explosion" of the "primeval atom" — what was later called the Big Bang. [R267]

Observation:

Aristotle accepted a universe having no beginning.

Jewish and Islamic philosophers required a beginning.

The redshifts from consistently measuring a velocity wrong resulted in what Aristotle considered unnecessary.

16.2 CMB

The cosmic microwave background (CMB, CMBR), in Big Bang cosmology, is electromagnetic radiation which is a remnant from an early stage of the universe, also known as "relic radiation". [R267]

Dr. Pierre-Marie Robitaille has published papers and produced YouTube videos thoroughly describing why the CMB was never detected and how this mistake resulted in misleading claims of its evidence. [R267]

17 Final Conclusion

The essential problem for astronomers is finding an acceptable velocity for an acceptable distance to calculate an acceptable value of Hubble's Constant.

Cosmology has several serious problems when measuring the velocity of distant galaxies and quasars.

Their velocities are measured like stars; this is mistake.

Every galaxy and quasar velocity value is wrong.

Only distances based on a standard candle like a variable star could remain valid.

Any distance based on a velocity is wrong.

The only way to measure a galaxy's velocity or a quasar's velocity in 3-dimensions, like left/right, up/down, forward / away (or in / out) is by taking many position measurements over a long time to divide distance by time.

All current galaxy and quasar velocities are invalid.

Only distances based on luminosity, when not using a redshift velocity, are valid. Using Cepheids is one example.

Therefore, nearly every galaxy and quasar distance must be withdrawn, because only a few have a justifiable distance, independent of a (wrong) velocity.

Astronomers must explain that we have never measured any galaxy's true motion. This is a direct contradiction to the decades of many claiming with certainty:

a) that the universe started with a big bang and space itself is somehow expanding faster than the speed of light,

b) that we know the exact age of the universe with fine precision.

Unfortunately, the scope of recovering from this mistake of measurement is close to starting over with most of what is beyond our Milky Way. This is almost like the misperception before 1924, when everything beyond our solar system was believed to be part of our Milky Way. Now, there is no correctly measured motion of anything beyond our Milky Way.

Many other mistakes like big bang, black holes, dark energy, dark matter, and Hubble's Law & constant, expansion must depart, as well. All are mistakes driven by accepting incorrect data or claims having no evidence.

As my other books noted, the recovery should also include the removal of relativity from cosmology and physics.

A new cosmology must be based on classical physics, as defined by Newton and Maxwell, and improved by Alfven.

My earlier book Redefining Gravity explains why Newton's real force of gravity must replace space-time from Einstein's relativity. Gravity must be redefined to be Newton's force, not space-time. My earlier book Cosmology Connections noted the many instances of electrical connections, like an aurora, which must be part of cosmology. [R270]

19 References

The references in the book are available as clickable links from a page in the author's web site.

1. Start web browser

2. Go to this site: www.cosmologyview.com

3. Make sure the browser is on the correct home page:

Cosmology Views

4. Scroll to near the middle.

5. Select: **Books by the author**

This page presents information for each book.

Locate the rows and columns for this book.

6. Locate: **Cosmology Crisis Cleared**

7. Below it, locate the date of this book's edition:

November 27, 2021 References

8. Select: **References** link after the correct date.

9. This selection presents a web page.

The page will list the references in the book by page number, with a link to that reference.

Each link indicates whether it is to a pdf, a YouTube video, or a URL link to a web page. The user is aware of what the browser will do with the link. Some browsers do a download of a pdf before its display.

Made in the USA
Monee, IL
05 December 2021

83672332R00154